FORMAL METHODS

SYNTHESE LIBRARY

A SERIES OF MONOGRAPHS ON THE

RECENT DEVELOPMENT OF SYMBOLIC LOGIC,

SIGNIFICS, SOCIOLOGY OF LANGUAGE,

SOCIOLOGY OF SCIENCE AND OF KNOWLEDGE,

STATISTICS OF LANGUAGE

AND RELATED FIELDS

Editors:

B. H. KAZEMIER / D. VUYSJE

EVERT W. BETH

FORMAL METHODS

AN INTRODUCTION TO SYMBOLIC LOGIC

AND TO THE STUDY OF EFFECTIVE OPERATIONS

IN ARITHMETIC AND LOGIC

D. REIDEL PUBLISHING COMPANY / DORDRECHT-HOLLAND

TO THE MEMORY OF MY MOTHER

TABLE OF CONTENTS

PREFACE

Many philosophers have considered logical reasoning as an inborn ability of mankind and as a distinctive feature in the human mind; but we all know that the distribution of this capacity, or at any rate its development, is very unequal. Few people are able to set up a cogent argument; others are at least able to follow a logical argument and even to detect logical fallacies. Nevertheless, even among educated persons there are many who do not even attain this relatively modest level of development.

According to my personal observations, lack of logical ability may be due to various circumstances. In the first place, I mention lack of general intelligence, insufficient power of concentration, and absence of formal education. Secondly, however, I have noticed that many people are unable, or sometimes rather unwilling, to argue *ex hypothesi*; such persons cannot, or will not, start from premises which they know or believe to be false or even from premises whose truth is not, in their opinion, sufficiently warranted. Or, if they agree to start from such premises, they sooner or later stray away from the argument into attempts first to settle the truth or falsehood of the premises. Presumably this attitude results either from lack of imagination or from undue moral rectitude.

On the other hand, proficiency in logical reasoning is not in itself a guarantee for a clear theoretic insight into the principles and foundations of logic. Skill in logical argumentation is the result of congenital ability combined with practice; theoretic insight, however, can only arise from reflection and analysis.

The purpose of this little book is not to remedy the above-mentioned wide-spread lack of logical ability. I very much doubt the possibility of a cure for lack of intelligence, power of concentration, or imagination. Lack of formal education can, of course, be remedied, but hardly by the study of logic alone. Perhaps this study can be helpful in overcoming the obstacles created by undue moral rectitude.

My main purpose in writing this book has been to explain the principles, foundations, and methods of logic in accordance with contemporary theoretic insight. I have attempted to present this rather subtle subject as simply as possible, but nevertheless I had to presuppose a certain amount of logical skill—about so much as will normally result from the study of elementary mathematics. No previous study of logical theory is required.

For various reasons, I have included a summary discussion of the formalization of arithmetic. But I have neither explained the circumstances which prompted modern developments in logical theory nor the philosophical implications of these developments. For these subjects I may refer to the companion volume on *Mathematical Thought*.

Although I have done my best to maintain a reasonable level of rigour, I have avoided pedantry, real or apparent, in this as well as in other respects. In some cases, I have deliberately and tacitly skipped certain explanations and even proofs, as they might divert the reader's attention from the main course of the argument. If possible, such omissions are made up for as soon as there is an opportunity to return to the subject. But sometimes it seemed better to defer the discussion to a special Section in the *Appendix*.

For those readers who are not professional logicians, the following remarks may be helpful. A book of this kind cannot be read quickly but must be studied carefully. If an isolated, relatively brief, passage presents serious difficulties, it may nevertheless be wise to go ahead and to return later on. If, however, at a certain point various difficulties turn up, this usually means that part of the preceding material has not been rightly understood; it is then advisable to start once more, say, at the beginning of the Section or Chapter.

No exercises are offered, but the reader will have no trouble in finding material by which to test his understanding. For instance, he should draw up deductive and semantic tableaux for the theses which are proved in Section 4. Conversely, he should construct formulas which are logical identities and then try to prove these formulas to be theses on the basis of the axioms stated in Sections 4, 7, and 10.

As to the Bibliography, it is not meant to encourage consulting other publications before the present book, or at least a substantial part of it, has been carefully studied. There still exist many differences in terminology, notation, and method of exposition which, to a certain extent, are motivated by underlying differences of opinion as to the purpose, the principles, and the proper method of logical theory. Unfortunately these differences make it difficult for a beginner to study several books at the same time. Of course, after completing his initiation the reader should try to find his way in the vast literature on the subject.

One final remark is rather meant for professional readers of this book. For classical elementary logic, and for the various logical systems more or less closely connected with it, at least three different methods of deduction are known today and are more or less currently applied in research: Hilbert-type deduction, Gentzen's natural deduction, and Gentzen's calculus of sequents. Logicians often tend to quarrel about the respective merits of these methods. In my opinion, discussions regarding this point are entirely out of place. It seems to me that they only continue because the disputants fail to grasp the fundamental unity of the three methods. In point of fact the three methods must rather be considered as different presentations of one and the same method.

It seems to me essential that a student of logic from the very beginning of his studies be taught all three methods and be made aware of the close connections which exist between them. Moreover, he should become acquainted both with the semantic and with the purely formal approach to the notions, the problems, and the results of logical theory. A dogmatic attitude with respect to the different aspects of logic will easily result if the elements of logic are taught in a narrow spirit.

Furthermore, if due attention is given to the aforementioned different aspects of logical theory, the subject becomes both more interesting and easier. Each one-sided approach leaves part of the material more or less in the dark. For instance, if the semantic background of the formal apparatus is not sufficiently explained, the student will fail to grasp the purpose of the proofs of completeness and thus many of the most important results of research in logic and foundations cannot be adequately understood. It should not be forgotten that later on it is extremely difficult to overcome the bad effects of a narrow-minded initiation.

I wish to express my indebtedness to Professor Hugh Leblanc of Bryn Mawr College who in 1957, by submitting the problem discussed in Section 40, *sub* (1), made me aware of the fact that certain aspects of the method of semantic tableaux deserved renewed attention. His remarks, together with other considerations, led to the introduction and discussion of deductive tableaux. Only after taking this step was I able to take full advantage of the ideas and results of the authors quoted in Section 6. I have also to thank my friends, Professor B. H. Kazemier and Dr. D. Vuysje, who by their invitation made it possible for me to present the results of my analysis in the form of a book. Miss E. M. Barth, Dr. K. L. de Bouvère, Mr. Horace S. Glover, Mr. J. J. F. Nieland, and Mr. S. C. van Westrhenen have studied the manuscript in various stages of development, and I have to thank them for many improvements both in form and in content. In addition, Miss Barth and Mr. Glover have given considerable help in proof-reading and so has also Mrs. Gay Honeywood.

E. W. BETH

Amsterdam, October, 1961.

REMARKS ON TERMINOLOGY AND NOTATION

The symbols and formulas appearing in the printed text of stipulations (F1)-(F3) in Section 1 (*cf.* Sections 7, 8, and 37) are best understood as names or descriptions of the symbols and formulas of logic, or as variables ranging over the sets of all these symbols and formulas. Likewise, the first and fourth formulas appearing in stipulation (F2^b) in Section 8 are to be understood, respectively, as variables ranging over the relevant subsets of the sets of all formulas and of all expressions of logic. The symbols and formulas of logic are only discussed, they are never actually displayed.

We also discuss finite sets K, L, (K', U), $(U_1, U_2, \ldots, U_m)$, $\ldots$ of logical formulas. A sequent K/L is an ordered couple of such sets (*cf.* Section 33) and *not*, as in Gentzen, a logical formula in its own right. Accordingly, no specific calculus of sequents is developed, but sequents and (deductive and semantic) tableaux are used as tools in the meta-mathematical analysis of certain logical systems. Practically, however, the study of deductive and semantic tableaux provides a convenient alternative to the metamathematical investigation of Gentzen's calculi LJ and LK.

The symbols appearing in the text of Section 17, *sub* (4), are meant to describe certain numerals which, in turn, are assumed to denote certain natural numbers.

By *semantics* I mean a rigorously deductive treatment of the connections between the logical and mathematical symbols and the objects which they denote. An informal discussion of the same subject is denoted as *hermeneutics*.

In connection with the discussion in the Preface, I may refer to similar remarks on lack of logical ability which are made by J. Castiello, *Geistesformung*, Berlin-Bonn 1934, Ss. 74–76.

The title of Section 19 must be understood in connection with the explanations given in Section 22, *sub* (1).

CHAPTER I

PURELY IMPLICATIONAL LOGIC

1. INTRODUCTION

Logic can be characterised as a *theory of inference*. In the present book we shall be concerned in particular with *deductive inference*, which plays such an important rôle in mathematics. As an example of a form of deductive inference, I mention the so-called *modus ponens*:

$$\textit{If U then V}$$
$$\underline{U}$$
$$\textit{Hence V}$$

which actually is to play an important rôle in our discussions.

An inference of this kind involves three *sentences*: two *premisses* and a *conclusion*. In the context of a particular inference, the internal structure of the second premiss U and of the conclusion V does not really matter. Therefore, instead of actually taking sentences, we may as well take letters (or *parameters*) which stand for sentences, just as in algebra we introduce letters which are to stand for numbers.

It is, however, essential that the first premiss be a certain compound sentence, namely, the *implication*, by the second premiss U, of the conclusion V. We imitate algebra further by substituting for the phrase '*if ... then*', a special symbol ' $\rightarrow$ ', thus writing: '$U \rightarrow V$' instead of: '*If U then V*'.

These two steps suggest, moreover, the construction of arbitrary *formulas* U, V, W, ..., starting from certain *atoms*: A, B, C, ... , in accordance with the following stipulations:

(F1) Each atom shall be a formula;

(F2) If both U and V are formulas, then $(U \rightarrow V)$ shall be a formula [actually, in writing compound formulas we shall not always strictly comply with this stipulation; in practice, it proves convenient to omit the outermost parentheses of compound formulas; however, if U or V is

1

a compound formula whose outermost parentheses have been omitted, then these parentheses must be restored before we can construct $(U \to V)$ which, in turn, is written $U \to V$. Moreover, it proves convenient to use $\{,\}$ and $[,]$ besides $(,)$];

(F3) Nothing shall be a formula, except on the strength of (F1) and (F2);

(F3') The set of all formulas is the *smallest* set K which fulfils the following conditions: (1) K contains all atoms $A, B, C, \ldots$; (2) whenever K contains both U and V, then K also contains $(U \to V)$;

(F3") U is a formula if and only if there exists a finite sequence of objects $U_1, U_2, \ldots, U_k$ such that, for each j ($1 \leq j \leq k$), either U_j is an atom or else we can find numbers m and n ($1 \leq m, n < j$) such that U_j is $(U_m \to U_n)$, whereas U_k is U.

Stipulation (F3) is clearly meant to prevent the introduction of formulas whose admission is not required under (F1) and (F2); however, it is formulated in legal rather than in logical terms. Therefore, the alternative formulations (F3') and (F3") have been adjoined. It is easy to see that (F3') is a paraphrase of (F3); a still better formulation consists in saying that the set of all formulas is the *intersection* of all sets K as described. Finally, (F3") expresses at the same time a convenient *criterion* for the admission of a given object U as a formula.

For instance, $[(A \to B) \to A] \to A$ is a formula because of the existence of a finite sequence consisting of:

$$U_1: \quad A, \text{ an atom,}$$
$$U_2: \quad B, \text{ an atom,}$$
$$U_3: \quad A \to B, \text{ or } U_1 \to U_2,$$
$$U_4: \quad (A \to B) \to A, \text{ or } U_3 \to U_1,$$
$$U_5: \quad [(A \to B) \to A] \to A, \text{ or } U_4 \to U_1.$$

Conversely, if for $[(\in \to A) \to A] \to \in$ we try to construct a suitable sequence, we obtain nothing better than:

$$U_1: \quad A,$$
$$U_2: \quad \in,$$
$$U_3: \quad \in \to A,$$
$$U_4: \quad (\in \to A) \to A,$$
$$U_5: \quad [(\in \to A) \to A] \to \in.$$

Since $\in$ is not an atom, it follows that $[(\in \to A) \to A] \to \in$ is not a formula.

2

An application of *modus ponens* will henceforth present itself as:

$$(\mathrm{i}^0) \quad \frac{\begin{array}{c} U \to V \\ U \end{array}}{V} \qquad \text{or} \qquad (\mathrm{i}^0) \quad \frac{\begin{array}{c} U \\ U \to V \end{array}}{V}$$

We shall now, for a moment, abandon the purely *deduction-theoretic* conception of inference and consider it from a *semantic* angle. Semantically speaking, we are interested in deductive inference because, whenever *true premisses* are given, the application of a valid form of inference produces a *true conclusion*. In the case of *modus ponens* this suggests that somehow the truth or falsehood (or, as we shall say, the *truth value*) of the conclusion V depends upon the truth values of the premisses $U \to V$ and U; or, conversely, that the truth value of the sentence $U \to V$ depends upon the truth values of U and V.

In ordinary language, no simple connection between the truth values of an implication and of its components can be established, because of the influence of the context in which these various sentences may appear. For our present purpose, however, a very simple connection can be established on the basis of the following *heuristic principles*:

 (I) Each of the sentences U, V, and $U \to V$ must be either *true* or *false*;
 (II) The truth value of a compound sentence $U \to V$ must be *uniquely determined* by the truth values of its components U and V;
(III) *Modus ponens* must be an admissible form of inference;
(IV) Proof by *reductio ad absurdum* must be possible;
 (V) It must be possible to apply an *argumentum ex hypothesi*.

ad (I)–(II) On account of these principles, our problem reduces to that of completing the following so-called *truth table*,

		V	
		T	F
U	T	(a)	(b)
	F	(c)	(d)

by supplying the appropriate entries (a)–(d).

ad (III) This principle provides for the entry (b). For, if both U and

3

$U \rightarrow V$ are true, then V must not be false; thus, if U is true and V is false, then $U \rightarrow V$ cannot be true and hence $U \rightarrow V$ must be false.

ad (IV) In such a proof, we start from an assumption U which later on turns out to be false. Nevertheless, the implications $U \rightarrow V$ which we establish must be true. A conclusion V obtained from a true premiss $U \rightarrow V$ and a false premiss U can, of course, be false, but it may also happen to be true. Thus, if U is false and V is either true or false, it must be possible that $U \rightarrow V$ is true; hence, by principle (II), $U \rightarrow V$ must always be true in these two cases. This remark provides for the entries (c) and (d).

ad (V) In order to establish a conclusion V, we often prove implications $U \rightarrow V$, without knowing whether the hypothesis U is true or false. Thus, if U is either true or false and V is true, it must be possible that $U \rightarrow V$ is true. Since, by principle (II), it follows that $U \rightarrow V$ is always true in these two cases, this remark provides for the entries (a) and (c). As a result, we obtain the familiar truth table:

		V	
		T	F
	T	T	F
U			
	F	T	T

For later use, we state the corresponding *semantic rule*:

(S1) If either U is false or V is true, then $U \rightarrow V$ is true; if U is true and V is false, then $U \rightarrow V$ is false.

There are formulas, for instance $A \rightarrow (B \rightarrow A)$ and $A \rightarrow [(A \rightarrow B) \rightarrow B]$, which are true by virtue of this rule alone; these formulas are called *logical identities* (sometimes *tautologies*, as if they could help it).

As these logical identities may be expected to play some special rôle in connection with deductive inference, one might reasonably consider the possibility of first embarking on a study of these formulas. This explains the existence of an *axiomatic approach* which may consist, for instance, in deriving all logical identities from certain axioms by means of *modus ponens*.

4

We have considered in turn three conceptions of logic as a theory of deductive inference: the purely *deduction-theoretic* (or *formalist*), the *semantic*, and the *axiomatic conception*. Each provides an approach to an independent development of logic. But there are considerable advantages in combining the various conceptions. In the first place, as the above introductory explanations suggest, there are certain connections between them; secondly, in order to obtain a complete understanding of logic, one must know them all; and, thirdly, a combination of the three conceptions makes the development of logic quite easy. Specifically, we shall start from the deduction-theoretic conception. When a certain point has been reached, we shall switch over to the semantic conception. Finally, we shall give an axiomatic treatment which will enable us to provide a synthesis of the three conceptions.

2. DEDUCTION-THEORETIC APPROACH

We shall first present some further heuristic considerations. A *deduction problem* may be characterised by a *sequent* K/L, or:

Premisses	Conclusions
K	L

where the *antecedent* K is a finite set of formulas U_1, U_2, ... , U_m whereas the *succedent* L will consist, for the time being, of a single formula Z. Such a sequent will be taken to express the problem of deducing the conclusion Z from the premisses U_1, U_2, ..., U_m in K.
We shall establish a number of schemata permitting the *reduction* of such a problem to simpler problems of the same kind and, eventually, the *closure* of a sequence of subsequent reductions which finally produces the proposed deduction. The reduction schemata will be based on the heuristic principle that, essentially, a premiss in the form of an implication $U \to V$ can only be used in a suitable application of *modus ponens*.

(1) First suppose we are dealing with the deduction problem $K/U \to V$. Then we argue as follows. If the problem can be solved, we should be able to deduce $U \to V$ from K. Now suppose we had instead the deduction

5

problem $(K, U)/V$. This problem would also be solvable; for we could first deduce, as before, $U \to V$ from K, and then we could use the additional premiss U in order to deduce V from $U \to V$ and U by *modus ponens*. Conversely, suppose the problem $(K, U)/V$ to be solvable; then nothing will happen if the problem $K/U \to V$ is taken to be solvable as well. For, if $U \to V$ is added to the premisses in K, we shall still need a premiss U before any conclusion can be drawn, and the conclusion V obtainable from $U \to V$ and U is anyhow deducible from (K, U); so we may safely replace the deduction problem $K/U \to V$ by the deduction problem $(K, U)/V$.

(2) If we are dealing with a deduction problem $(K', U \to V)/Z$ then, in order to take advantage of the premiss $U \to V$, we wish to deduce V from $U \to V$ and U. But this requires that we first deduce U from $(K', U \to V)$. So the initial problem splits into two problems, namely:
  (i) From $(K', U \to V)$, deduce U [and then V by *modus ponens*];
  (ij) From $(K' U \to V, V)$, deduce Z.
Let us apply these devices in a discussion of the deduction problem characterized by the sequent $(A \to B, B \to C)/A \to C$.

Premisses	Conclusions
(1) $A \to B$	(3) $A \to C$
(2) $B \to C$	Instead of deducing (3) directly

from (1) and (2), we add the formula:
(4) A	to the premisses and we try to
deduce the conclusion:	(5) C

from the premisses (1), (2), and (4). Then, in order to take advantage of the premiss (1), we split our problem into two new ones:

(i)	(ij)	(i)	(ij)
	(7) B	(6) A	(5) C

The first, under (i), consists in deducing, from the premisses (1), (2), and (4), the conclusion (6) [and then, by *modus ponens*, (7)]. The second, under (ij), consists in deducing, from the premisses (1), (2), (4), and (7), the conclusion (5). However, problem (i) is trivial because premiss (4)

6

coincides with conclusion (6). We draw double horizontal lines to show that problem (i) has been solved.

In problem (ij), we wish to take advantage of premiss (2). So our problem splits once more into new ones, both of which prove trivial:

(iij)	(iv)	(iij)	(iv)
	(9) C	(8) B	(5) C

(3) Our discussion clearly consists in a repeated application of three typical operations which can be characterized by the following schemata.

$$
(i) \quad
\begin{array}{c|c}
\text{Premisses} & \text{Conclusions} \\ \hline
K' & Z \\
Z & \\
\end{array}
$$

$$
(ij^{aI}) \quad
\begin{array}{cc|cc}
\multicolumn{2}{c|}{\text{Premisses}} & \multicolumn{2}{c}{\text{Conclusions}} \\ \hline
\multicolumn{2}{c|}{K'} & \multicolumn{2}{c}{Z} \\
\multicolumn{2}{c|}{U \to V} & & \\ \hline
(i) & (ij) & (i) & (ij) \\
& V & U & Z \\
\end{array}
\qquad
(ij^{b}) \quad
\begin{array}{c|c}
\text{Premisses} & \text{Conclusions} \\ \hline
K & U \to V \\
U & V \\
\end{array}
$$

Schema (i), the *closure schema*, expresses the fact that, if the conclusion coincides with one of the premisses, then the deduction problem is a trivial one and so the search for a solution may be terminated. The *reduction schema* (ij^{aI}) represents the tactics by which we try to take advantage of a premiss $U \to V$. It may be observed that these tactics involved an application of *modus ponens* which is not expressed by the schema. In point of fact, by accepting reduction schema (ij^{aI}) we tacitly express, so to speak, our acceptance of *modus ponens*.

The *reduction schema* (ij^{b}) represents the tactics by which we try to establish a conclusion $U \to V$.

(4) As a result of the above heuristic considerations we can now state the following requirements (i)–(iij) which any *adequate method of formal deduction* can be reasonably expected to fulfil. The statement of these

7

requirements, however, is *not* meant to form part of our heuristics; we rather stipulate that we shall not accept any method of formal deduction unless it fulfils at least the requirements (i)–(iij).

(i) An adequate method of formal deduction should enable us to consider deduction problems characterized by sequents K/Z;

(ij) It should in some way or other make allowance for the reduction of deduction problems in accordance with the reduction schemata (ij^{aI}) and (ij^b);

(iij) It should in some manner provide for a successful termination of a deduction under the closure schema (i).

Of course, it does *not* immediately follow from our considerations that there exists any adequate method of deduction. Nevertheless, these considerations provide a certain insight into various properties which every adequate method of deduction must possess. For instance, it makes possible a solution to the deduction problem characterized by the sequent $(A \to B, B \to C)/A \to C$. This can be seen from the following diagram.

	Premisses		Conclusions	
(ij^b)	(1) $A \to B$		(3) $A \to C$	
	(2) $B \to C$			
(ij^{aI})	(4) A		(5) C	
	(i)	(ij)	(i)	(ij)
(i)		(7) B	(6) A	(5) C
(ij^{aI})				
	(iij)	(iv)	(iij)	(iv)
(i)		(9) C	(8) B	(5) C

This diagram is clearly nothing else but a more systematic version of our informal discussion under (2). It shows that under reduction schemata (ij^{aI}) and (ij^b) the proposed deduction can be reduced to a few *subordinate deductions* each of which is amenable to an application of the closure schema (i).

A similar diagram can be drawn up for *every* deduction problem characterized by a sequent (many more examples will be offered later on). Such a diagram will be called a *deductive tableau* for the given sequent.

(5) We can now easily exhibit at least one example of an adequate method of formal deduction as characterized by the above requirements (i)–(iij): for every sequent we shall accept as a *formal deduction* any deductive tableau drawn up in accordance with reduction schemata (ij^{aI}) and (ij^b) and showing every subordinate deduction to be completed under the closure schema (i).

For instance, the above deductive tableau provides a formal deduction as proposed by the sequent $(A \to B, B \to C)/A \to C$ which we took as an example.

3. SEMANTIC APPROACH

It sometimes proves convenient to say that $w(U) = 2$ or $w(U) = 0$ according as U is true or false, and to denote the numbers 0 and 2 as *truth values*. Using this terminology, we can restate our above semantic rule as follows:

(S1) If $w(U) = 0$ or $w(U) = 2$, then $w(U \to V) = 2$; if $w(U) = 2$ and $w(V) = 0$, then $w(U \to V) = 0$.

On account of this rule the truth values $w(U)$ of all formulas U will be uniquely determined as soon as for each atom $A, B, C, \ldots$ an arbitrary truth value $w(A), w(B), w(C). \ldots$ (which must be either 0 or 2) has been specified; we shall say that by each specification of these truth values a *valuation w* is established. [In most cases, we shall be interested only in the truth values taken by the formulas in some finite set; these truth values depend only upon the values given to those finitely many atoms $A, B, \ldots$ which actually appear in those formulas. The values $w(A), w(B), \ldots$ define a *partial valuation* which assigns a definite truth value $w(U)$ only to those formulas U in which no other atoms appear.] If U is a *logical identity*, as defined in Section 1, then we have $w(U) = 2$ for every valuation w, and conversely.

If K and L are finite sets of formulas $U_1, U_2, \ldots, U_m$ and $V_1, V_2, \ldots, V_n$, respectively, then the *valuation problem* characterized by the sequent K/L, or

True	False
K	L

9

will consist in specifying, if possible, a valuation w under which all formulas in K are true and all formulas in L are false.

As a concrete example, we consider the valuation problem characterized by the sequent $(A \to B, B \to C)/A \to C$. The '*official*' manner, so to speak, of dealing with such a problem consists in constructing a truth table, as follows.

A	B	$A \to B$	C	$B \to C$	$A \to C$
0	0	2	0	2	2
2	0	0	0	2	0
0	2	2	0	0	2
2	2	2	0	0	0
0	0	2	2	2	2
2	0	0	2	2	2
0	2	2	2	2	2
2	2	2	2	2	2

The table clearly shows that *no* valuation as required can be found. There is, however, a different approach to valuation problems which in many respects is more convenient than the 'official' approach. We advance, in connection with our example, the following discussion.

True	False
(1) $A \to B$	(3) $A \to C$
(2) $B \to C$	In order to make formula (3) false,
we have to make formula	
(4) A	true, and at the same time formula
	(5) C

false. Then, in order to make formula (1) true, we must either (i) make formula (6) false, or (ij) make formula (7) true; accordingly, our problem splits into two new ones:

(i)	(ij)	(i)	(ij)
	(7) B	(6) A	

But it is clearly impossible to find a valuation which makes formula (4) true and at the same time makes formula (6) false. So problem (i) is

10

trivially unsolvable, which we show by drawing double horizontal lines:

In problem (ij), we consider the possibilities of making formula (2) true. Once more our problem splits into two new ones, which both prove trivially unsolvable:

(iij)	(iv)	(iij)	(iv)
	(9) C	(8) B	

Again our discussion consists in a repeated application of three typical operations which are characterized by the following schemata.

	True	False
	K'	L'
(i)	U	U

(ija)	True		False	
	K'		L	
	$U \to V$			
	(i)	(ij)	(i)	(ij)
		V	U	

(ijb)	True	False
	K	L'
		$U \to V$
	U	V

A few words may be said in explanation of each of these schemata.

ad (i) The closure here expresses the fact that the valuation problem characterized by the sequent $(K', U)/(L', U)$ is *not* solvable, in other words, that no (partial) valuation as required is available; there can clearly be no valuation w under which both $w(U) = 2$ and $w(U) = 0$. It should, perhaps, be emphasized that the relative order of the formulas in the sets (K', U) and (L', U) does not matter; in particular, it is not required (as suggested by the schema) that U be the *last* formula. This remark holds also for the schemata (ija) and (ijb).

ad (ija) As $U \to V$ is true if, and only if, either U is false or V is true, it will be clear that the valuation problem $(K', U \to V)/L$ reduces to the two problems $(K', U \to V)/(L, U)$ and $(K', U \to V, V)/L$.

ad (ijb) Likewise, as $U \to V$ is false if, and only if, U is true and V is false, the valuation problem $K/(L', U \to V)$ reduces to the problem $(K, U)/(L', U \to V, V)$.

11

Using these *closure* and *reduction schemata* for valuation problems, we can replace our above informal discussion of the valuation problem characterized by the sequent $(A \rightarrow B, B \rightarrow C)/A \rightarrow C$ by the following diagram.

	True		False	
(ij^b)	(1) $\quad A \rightarrow B$		(3) $\quad A \rightarrow C$	
	(2) $\quad B \rightarrow C$			
	(4) $\quad A$		(5) $\quad C$	
(ij^a)	(i)	(ij)	(i)	(ij)
		(7) B	(6) A	
(i)				
(ij^a)	(iij)	(iv)	iij	(iv)
		(9) C	(8) B	
(i)				

A similar diagram can be drawn up for each valuation problem characterized by a sequent K/L; it will be called a *semantic tableau* for the given sequent.

(1) It will be clear that, unless K and L contain only atomic formulas, any given valuation problem K/L can be submitted to successive reductions. Moreover, if a schema (ij^a) or (ij^b) has been applied, then further on the formula $U \rightarrow V$ involved can be disregarded. It follows that, provided the reduction schemata are applied sufficiently often, all formulas in K and in L will finally be decomposed into atoms, and then further reductions will be useless. Once this stage has been reached, there are two possibilities:

(I) Each of the *final subordinate sequents* which result from the reductions is amenable to an application of the closure schema (i).

(II) At least one of the final subordinate sequents cannot be closed.

(2) With case (I) we have already met in our above example. So let us also consider, before discussing the two cases more systematically, a concrete example of case (II). We take the valuation problem characterized by the sequent $\emptyset/[(A \rightarrow B) \rightarrow B] \rightarrow B$; by $\emptyset$ we denote the empty set. We obtain the following diagram.

	True		False	
(ij^b)			(1) $[(A \to B) \to B] \to B$	
(ij^a)	(2) $(A \to B) \to B$		(3) B	
	(i)	(ij)	(i)	(ij)
		(5) B	(4) $A \to B$	
(i)				
(ij^b)				
	(6) A		(7) B	

The final subordinate sequent under (i) cannot be closed. As all formulas have been decomposed into atoms, it makes no sense to apply further reductions.

(3) We shall now present a more systematic discussion of the two cases (I) and (II).

ad (I) As each of the final subordinate sequents is amenable to an application of the closure schema (i), none of the corresponding valuation problems admits of a solution. Hence, by our above justification of the reduction schemata, the initial problem K/L which has been reduced to these problems, also cannot be solved. In other words: whenever under a valuation w *all* formulas U in K are true, then under that valuation w at least one of the formulas V in L must also be true.

ad (II) Each of those final subordinate sequents which cannot be closed provides a partial valuation w as required.

Before showing this in general, let us return to our example and isolate that particular final subordinate sequent which is not closed.

True	False
	(1) $[(A \to B) \to B] \to B$
(2) $(A \to B) \to B$	(3) B
	(4) $A \to B$
(6) A	(7) B

This diagram plainly suggests that, by taking $w(A) = 2$, $w(B) = 0$, we shall obtain $w\{[(A \to B) \to B] \to B\} = 0$, as required. Let us check this remark by the *'official'* method.

13

A	B	$A \to B$	$(A \to B) \to B$	$[(A \to B) \to B] \to B$
0	0	2	0	2
2	0	0	2	0
0	2	2	2	2
2	2	2	2	2

However, this computation, though reassuring, is completely superfluous. For the above diagram has been constructed in such a manner that, in inverse order, it represents the same computation which in the *official* truth table appears on the second line.

Now let us consider, in general, an arbitrary non-closed final subordinate sequent K^0/L^0 for a valuation problem K/L. We observe, in the first place, that $K \subseteq K^0$ and $L \subseteq L^0$. Let us define the following (partial) valuation w: if an atom X appears in K^0, then $w(X) = 2$, if not, than $w(X) = 0$. We wish to show that for all formulas U in K^0, we have $w(U) = 2$, and that for all formulas V in L^0, we have $w(V) = 0$. Let us denote any formula as *wrongly placed*, if it is in K^0 but false, or in L^0 but true; then we have to show: no formula is *wrongly placed*.

(i) Suppose $Y \to Z$ to be wrongly placed in K^0; then we have $w(Y \to Z) = 0$, hence $w(Y) = 2$, $w(Z) = 0$. Moreover, the presence of a formula $Y \to Z$ in an antecedent permits an application of reduction schema (ij^a) and, as K^0/L^0 is final, it follows that the reduction has been carried out. As a result, either Y must appear in L^0 or Z must appear in K^0; accordingly, either Y or Z is wrongly placed.

(ij) Suppose $Y \to Z$ to be wrongly placed in L^0; then we have $w(Y \to Z) = 2$, hence either $w(Y) = 0$ or $w(Z) = 2$. Moreover, as a result of an application of reduction schema (ij^b), Y appears in K^0 and Z appears in L^0. Therefore, either Y or Z is wrongly placed.

(iij) It clearly follows from (i) and (ij) that, whenever a compound formula $Y \to Z$ is wrongly placed, some atom must be wrongly placed. However, because of the choice of the valuation w, no atom can be wrongly placed; in this connection it may be observed that no atom can appear both in K^0 and in L^0, because otherwise we could apply the closure schema (i).

Remark. Strictly speaking, the above argument is superfluous. For under (1) we have already observed that, if a schema (ij^a) or (ij^b) has been

14

applied, then further on the corresponding formula can be disregarded. Thus, as K^0/L^0 is final, all compound formulas can be disregarded. So it is sufficient to observe that, under the above choice of the valuation w, no atom is wrongly placed.

(iv) As $K \subseteq K^0$ and $L \subseteq L^0$, it will be clear that $w(U) = 2$ for all formulas U in K and $w(V) = 0$ for all formulas V in L.

(4) From the very nature of valuation problems it follows that for the final result it does not matter in what *relative order* the various formulas $Y \rightarrow Z$ in K or L are singled out to be '*treated*' under the reduction schemata. Secondly, it will be clear from our discussion that all reduction steps are *reversible*.

For each valuation problem K/L we can draw up a diagram which is called its *semantic tableau* and which shows all successive reductions as well as all closures of final subordinate sequents. So far two examples were given; more examples will be given later on.

(5) There is a striking similarity between the reduction and closure schemata for deduction and for valuation problems. But before we try to take advantage of this similarity, it will be appropriate to state the differences, namely:

(a) In deduction problems K/L, the succedent L consists of a single formula Z, whereas, in valuation problems K/L, the succedent L may contain any finite number of formulas.

(b) In the subordinate sequent (i) which results from an application of reduction schema (ij^{aI}) for deduction problems, the initial conclusion is supplanted by the formula U, whereas in reduction schema (ij^a) for valuation problems, the formula U is added to the initial succedent L.

(c) In the case of a deduction problem K/L the closure of all final subordinate sequents K^0/L^0 shows that the proposed deduction can be carried out, whereas in the case of a valuation problem it shows, to the contrary, that no suitable valuation can be found.

(6) Now let us, for the time being, overlook differences (a) and (b); more precisely, let us agree to apply the reduction schemata for valuation problems also in dealing with deduction problems. Then any sequent K/L can be taken to characterize both a deduction and a valuation prob-

lem. By the discussion under (1), we may distinguish two cases (I) and (II) which can now be characterized as follows.

(I) The deduction proposed by the sequent K/L can be carried out.

(II) There is a valuation w such that $w(U) = 2$ for all formulas U in K and $w(V) = 0$ for all formulas V in L.

Since, for each sequent K/L, we have exactly one of these cases, it follows that:

(iv) If the deduction proposed by the sequent K/L can be carried out then, for each valuation w such that $w(U) = 2$ for every formula U in K, we have $w(V) = 2$ for at least one formula V in L; in particular, if the succedent L consists of a single formula Z then, *for each valuation w such that $w(U) = 2$ for every formula U in K, we have $w(Z) = 2$*;

(v) If, for a given sequent K/L, it is the case that, for each valuation w such that $w(U) = 2$ for every formula U in K, we have $w(V) = 2$ for at least one formula V in L, then the deduction proposed by that sequent can be carried out.

Condition (iv) expresses the '*soundness*' of a method of formal deduction; if this condition is not fulfilled, then it may happen that a false conclusion Z is deducible from a set K of true premisses. Condition (v) expresses the '*completeness*' of a method of formal deduction; if it is not fulfilled, then it may happen that, even though a certain formula Z cannot be false if all formulas in a certain set K are true, the formula Z is not formally deducible from the premisses in K.

Let us add these conditions (iv) and (v) to the requirements (i)-(iij) which we stated in Section 2, *sub* (4), and let us agree to accept as a *fully adequate method of formal deduction* any method which fulfils all requirements (i)-(v).

(7) It will be clear that we shall obtain a fully adequate method of formal deduction if, for each sequent K/L, we accept as a corresponding formal deduction any semantic tableau for this sequent, drawn up in accordance with reduction schemata (ij^a) and (ij^b) and showing each subordinate deduction to be completed under the closure schema (i).

(8) It is only reasonable to ask if we could not, alternatively, rely on deductive tableaux as described in Section 2, *sub* (4), that is, if we could not replace schema (ij^a) by schema (ij^{aI}).

16

The answer to this question is negative. A case in point is the sequent $\emptyset/[(A \to B) \to A] \to A$; let us construct both the deductive and the semantic tableau for this sequent.

	Premisses	Conclusions	
		(1) [...] $\to A$	
(ijᵇ)			
(ijᵃᴵ)	(2)(...)$\to A$	(3) A	
	(i) | (ij)	(i) | (ij)	
	| (5) A	(4) $A \to B$ | (3) A	
(i)			
(ijᵇ)			
(ijᵃᴵ)	(6) A	(7) B	
	(iij) | (iv)	(iij) | (iv)	
	| (9) A	(8) $A \to B$ | (7) B	
(ijᵇ)			
	(10) A	(11) B	

	True	False	
		(1) [...] $\to A$	
(ijᵇ)			
(ijᵃ)	(2)(...)$\to A$	(3) A	
	(i) | (ij)	(i) | (ij)	
	| (5) A	(4) $A \to B$	
(i)			
(ijᵇ)			
(i)	(6) A	(7) B	

In the first place, we observe that, in constructing these two tableaux, there is at each stage only one schema which can be applied; therefore, there is no need to discuss alternative constructions.

Secondly, we have to explain why the second application of the closure schema (i), which completes the semantic tableau, is not possible in the deductive tableau. In the semantic tableau, the succedent in the subordinate sequent (i) contains the formulas (1), (3), and (4); the second application of schema (ijᵇ) adds formula (6) to the antecedent and, hence, the presence of formulas (6) in the antecedent and (3) in the succedent brings about the closure. In the deductive tableau, however, the succedent in the subordinate sequent (i) consists only of the formula (4); the second application of schema (ijᵇ) adds formula (6) to the antecedent, whereas formula (4) is supplanted by formula (7). So formula (3) is not available in this case.

Finally, it will be clear that it makes no sense to continue the construction of the deductive tableau beyond the stage which has been reached. Both subordinate sequents (iij) and (iv) have $(A \to B) \to A$ and A in the antecedent and B in the succedent and hence no progress has been made with respect to the subordinate sequent (i). Further application of reduction schemata will not change the situation. – It follows that the deductive tableau will never yield a deduction as proposed.

17

(9) It will now be convenient to sum up the results achieved so far. Starting from heuristic principles borrowed from deduction theory, we stated the requirements (i)–(iij) to be fulfilled by any *adequate method of formal deduction*. Moreover, we found that the construction of (closed) *deductive tableaux* for sequents K/Z provided an adequate method of formal deduction in accordance with requirements (i)–(iij).

Semantical considerations suggested two further requirements (iv) and (v); any *fully adequate method of formal deduction* was to fulfil all requirements (i)–(v). We found that the construction of (closed) *semantic tableaux* for sequents K/L provided a fully adequate method of formal deduction in accordance with requirements (i)–(v); as the method of semantic tableaux fulfils the requirements (i)–(iij), it provides *a fortiori* an adequate method of formal deduction as described in Section 2, *sub* (4).

But the method of deductive tableaux made no provision for the deduction proposed by the sequent $\emptyset/[(A \to B) \to A] \to A$; therefore, it does not fulfil requirement (v) and so it cannot be accepted as a fully adequate method of formal deduction. Nevertheless it provides exactly for those deductions which are acceptable from an intuitionistic point of view. In point of fact, the formula $[(A \to B) \to A] \to A$, which is known as *Peirce's Law*, is, although classically a logical identity, not universally valid from an intuitionistic viewpoint.

(10) Now let us consider the diagram below.

Premisses		Conclusions	
K'		Z	
$U \to V$			
$[\bar{Z}]$	$[Z]$	Z	
(i)	(ij)	(i)	(ij)
$[\bar{U}]$	$[U]$	U	Z
⋮	V	⋮	
		$[Z]$	

(with row label (ij^{aI}))

Accordingly, the strengthening of our method of deduction which results if schema (ij^{aI}) is replaced by schema (ij^a) can also be obtained by an appeal to the principle of the excluded third [another device will be explained in Section 5, *sub* (1)]. Before applying reduction schema (ij$^\text{aI}$) we form two subordinate sequents by adding, respectively, $\bar{Z}$ and Z to the antecedent $(K', U \to V)$; the second sequent is immediately closed. The subsequent application of schema (ij$^\text{aI}$) is construed to consist in forming two subordinate sequents (i) and (ij) by adding, respectively, $\bar{U}$ and (U, V) to the antecedent $(K', U \to V, \bar{Z})$ whereas in the succedent of (i) the formula Z is supplanted by U. But the fact that Z is supplanted by U is no longer a source of trouble, because the appearance of $\bar{Z}$ in the antecedent permits us to insert Z in the succedent whenever this is convenient. And because $\bar{U}$ also appears in the antecedent of (i) we can again have U in the succedent whenever this is preferable. [Of course, this whole discussion would be out of place in a systematic development of purely implicational logic; but as part of our heuristics it is clearly acceptable.]

(11) We have seen that closed deductive or semantic tableaux can be considered as formal deductions. But it cannot be denied that they hardly present the shape in which deductions normally appear; we expect a deduction to start from the premisses and then somehow to work toward the conclusion. I now wish to show how closed tableaux can be rewritten as regular deductions. Let us first consider the deduction proposed by the sequent $(A \to B, B \to C)\,/A \to C$.

$$
\begin{array}{lll}
(1) & A \to B & [\text{premiss}] \\
(2) & B \to C & [\text{premiss}] \\
\hline
(4) & A & [+\,\text{hyp}\,1] \\
(8) & B & (1), \quad (4) \\
(5) & C & (2), \quad (8) \\
\hline
(3) & A \to C & [-\,\text{hyp}\,1]
\end{array}
$$

This is a completely normal deduction. After stating the premisses (1) and (2), we introduce the hypothesis (4) and then obtain formulas (8) and (5) by *modus ponens*. We eliminate the hypothesis by stating, in formula (3), the conclusion (5) '*under*' the hypothesis (4). The part of the deduction '*affected*' by the hypothesis is marked off by horizontal lines. Before similarly rewriting the semantic tableau for the sequent

19

$\emptyset/[(A \to B) \to A] \to A$, we apply the device described under (10) so as to prevent formula (3) from being supplanted.

	True		False	
(ij^b)			(1) $[(A \to B) \to A] \to A$	
	(2) $(A \to B) \to A$			
(ij^a)	(3') $[\bar{A}]$		(3) A	
	(i)	(ij)	(i)	(ij)
		(5) A	(4) $A \to B$	
(i)				
(ij^b)				
	(6) A		(7) B	
			(3'') $[A]$	
(i)				

The tableau thus obtained can be treated as a deductive tableau.

$$
\begin{array}{lll}
& (2)\ (A \to B) \to A & [+\text{hyp}\,1] \\
(i)\ \begin{array}{|l} (3')\ \bar{A} \\ (6)\ A \\ (7)\ B \\ (4)\ A \to B \end{array} & & \begin{array}{l} [+\text{hyp}\,2] \\ [+\text{hyp}\,3] \\ (3'),\ (6) \\ [-\text{hyp}\,3] \end{array} \\
(ij)\ \begin{array}{|l} (5)\ A \\ (3)\ A \end{array} & & \begin{array}{l} (2),\ (4) \\ [-\text{hyp}\,2] \end{array} \\
& (1)\ [(A \to B) \to A] \to A & [-\text{hyp}\,1]
\end{array}
$$

This is again a normal deduction, although a more interesting one. We first introduce three hypotheses: (2), (3'), and (6). Then, by the principle: *ex falso sequitur quodlibet*, we obtain (7) from (3') and (6). We now eliminate hypothesis (6) and get formula (4). Formula (5) results from (2) and (4) by *modus ponens*; this conclusion contradicts hypothesis (3') which is thus refuted. Therefore it is eliminated and formula (3) is obtained. The elimination of hypothesis (2) finally yields formula (1) as a conclusion. The parts of the deduction which are affected by the various hypotheses are again marked off. Moreover, I have indicated the two subordinate deductions which correspond to the application of reduction schema (ij^a).

The deductions resulting from systematically rewriting deductive and semantic tableaux belong, respectively, to certain logical systems F_0 and F which are closely related to Gentzen's systems NJ and NK. They have been studied elsewhere and will be only briefly discussed in Section 40.

(12) Let us consider the two diagrams below.

	True		False				True	False
	K		L'				K	L'
(ij^b)			$(U \to V) \to V$		(ij^c)			$(U \to V) \to V$
	$U \to V$		V					U
(ij^a)	(i)	(ij)	(i)	(ij)				V
		V	U					
(i)								

The left diagram is a semantic tableau drawn up in accordance with the reduction and closure schemata as stated above. These schemata make no allowance for the construction of the right diagram. However, it would not affect the final result of a tableau construction if this step were permitted. Thus we may introduce schema (ij^c) as a *derived reduction schema*.

(13) We still compare the following diagrams.

	True	False		True	False
	K	$\emptyset$	(ij^d)	K	$\emptyset$
					F

F must be an atom which does not occur in any of the formulas in K.

Any solution of a valuation problem $K/\emptyset$ yields a solution of the valuation problem K/F, and conversely; for any partial valuation w such that $w(U) = 2$ for any formula U in K can be extended by taking $w(F) = 0$.

So we may adopt schema (ij^d) as another *derived reduction schema*.

(14) We can now eliminate one of the differences between deduction and valuation problems as mentioned under (5). For, if in a valuation

21

problem K/L the succedent L consists of several formulas $V, W, \ldots, X$, then we may consider instead the valuation problem K/Z, where Z is the formula $((\ldots((V \to W) \to W) \to \ldots) \to X) \to X$. And, if the succedent L is the empty set $\varnothing$, then we may consider instead the valuation problem K/F, where F is an atom which does not appear in any of the formulas in K.

(15) I now give a few practical hints concerning the most efficient manner of using deductive and semantic tableaux. It is always best to postpone, as far as possible, reductions under schema (ij^a). If all reductions under schema (ij^b) have been carried out, then we select the first formula to be '*treated*' under schema (ij^a) in such a way that at least one of the subordinate sequents which result is quickly closed.

One may sometimes be tempted to arrange the parts of a tableau in a way which differs from that suggested by our examples. As a bad example I construct a tableau for the sequent $(A \to B, B \to C)/A \to C$, as follows.

[Incorrect]

	True		False	
	(1) $A \to B$		(3) $A \to C$	
	(2) $B \to C$			
(ij^b)				
(ij^a)	(4) A		(5) C	
	(i)		(ij)	
(ij^a)		(6) A	(7) B	
			(iii)	(iv)
			(8) B	(9) C

Such an arrangement tends to obscure the connections between a sequent and its subordinate sequents. Practically, it may make us overlook possible closures.

4. AXIOMATIC APPROACH

As before, S, T, U, V, W, X, Y, Z shall be arbitrary formulas as characterized by the stipulations (F1–3) in Section 1. As *axioms* we adopt *all* (infinitely many) formulas:

(I) $$U \to (V \to U),$$

(II) $$[U \to (V \to W)] \to [(U \to V) \to (U \to W)],$$

(III) $$[(U \to V) \to U] \to U.$$

For instance, the following formulas are axioms:

$$U \to (U \to U),$$
$$U \to \{(U \to U) \to U\},$$
$$(V \to W) \to [U \to (V \to W)],$$

because they have the structure characterized by (I), whereas the formula:

$$[U \to \{(U \to U) \to U\}] \to [\{U \to (U \to U)\} \to (U \to U)]$$

is an axiom because it has the structure characterized by (II).
As a *rule of inference* we adopt *modus ponens*, which can be indifferently represented by the *inference schemata*:

$$(i) \quad \frac{U \to V \quad U}{V} \qquad \text{and} \qquad (i) \quad \frac{U \quad U \to V}{V}$$

Those formulas which can be obtained, starting from certain axioms, by applying again and again the rule of inference, will be denoted as *theses*. In other words, the concept of a thesis is characterized by the following stipulations:

(T1) Each axiom is a thesis;
(T2) If both U and $U \to V$ are theses, then V is also a thesis;
(T3) Nothing is a thesis, except on the strength of (T1) and (T2).

As (F3) in Section 1, (T3) could be stated more precisely, but we shall not dwell on this point.

(1) We shall first establish two *derived inference schemata*, namely:

$$(ij) \quad \frac{U}{V \to U} \qquad \text{and} \qquad (iij) \quad \frac{U \to V \quad V \to W}{U \to W}$$

23

ad (ij) We have to show that, whenever U is a thesis, so also is $V \to U$; this we do as follows.

$$U \to (V \to U) \qquad \text{[axiom (I)]}$$

$$\text{(i)} \quad \frac{U}{V \to U} \qquad \text{[supposition]}$$

In order to avoid lengthy explanations, we shall often find it expedient to present our proofs in a certain standard form. The idea that a certain formula is a thesis is expressed by simply exhibiting that formula. If necessary, we indicate our reasons for considering a formula as a thesis at the *right* side of that formula, in [ ]. On the other hand, if a formula has been found to be a thesis, then we write a numeral at its *left* for reference.

ad (iij) We have to show that whenever both $U \to V$ and $V \to W$ are theses, so also is $U \to W$.

$$\text{(ij)} \quad \frac{V \to W}{U \to (V \to W)} \qquad \text{[supposition]}$$

$$\text{(i)} \quad \frac{[U \to (V \to W)] \to [(U \to V) \to (U \to W)]}{(U \to V) \to (U \to W)} \qquad \text{[axiom (II)]}$$

$$\text{(i)} \quad \frac{U \to V}{U \to W} \qquad \text{[supposition]}$$

(2) We now prove:

(IV) $\qquad\qquad\qquad U \to U$

Proof. $[U \to \{(U \to U) \to U\}] \to [\{U \to (U \to U)\} \to (U \to U)]$ [axiom (II)]

$$\text{(i)} \quad \frac{U \to \{(U \to U) \to U\}}{\{U \to (U \to U)\} \to (U \to U)} \qquad \text{[axiom (I)]}$$

$$\text{(i)} \quad \frac{U \to (U \to U)}{U \to U} \qquad \text{[axiom (I)]}$$

(V) $\qquad\qquad (V \to W) \to [(U \to V) \to (U \to W)]$

Proof. $\qquad\qquad (V \to W) \to [U \to (V \to W)]$ [axiom (I)]

$$\text{(iij)} \quad \frac{[U \to (V \to W)] \to [(U \to V) \to (U \to W)]}{(V \to W) \to [(U \to V) \to (U \to W)]} \qquad \text{[axiom (II)]}$$

24

We leave it to the reader to establish the derived inference schemata:

$$\text{(i}^{\text{a}})\ \frac{\begin{array}{c}S \to (U \to V)\\ S \to U\end{array}}{S \to V} \qquad \text{and} \qquad \text{(iv)}\ \frac{U \to V}{(S \to U) \to (S \to V)}$$

[the first one is easily obtained from axiom (II), and the second is connected with thesis (V)] and turn immediately to:

$$\text{(iij}^{\text{a}})\ \frac{\begin{array}{c}S \to (U \to V)\\ S \to (V \to W)\end{array}}{S \to (U \to W)}$$

ad (iij^{a})

$$\text{(iv)}\ \frac{(V \to W) \to [(U \to V) \to (U \to W)]}{\{S \to (V \to W)\} \to \{S \to [(U \to V) \to (U \to W)]\}} \qquad \text{[thesis (V)]}$$

$$\text{(i)}\ \frac{S \to (V \to W)}{S \to [(U \to V) \to (U \to W)]} \qquad \text{[supposition]}$$

$$\text{(i}^{\text{a}})\ \frac{S \to (U \to V)}{S \to (U \to W)} \qquad \text{[supposition]}$$

(VI) $\qquad [U \to (V \to W)] \to [V \to (U \to W)]$

Proof.
$$\text{(ij)}\ \frac{V \to (U \to V)}{[U \to (V \to W)] \to [V \to (U \to V)]} \qquad \text{[axiom (I)]}$$

$$\text{(iij}^{\text{a}})\ \frac{[U \to (V \to W)] \to [(U \to V) \to (U \to W)]}{[U \to (V \to W)] \to [V \to (U \to W)]} \qquad \text{[axiom (II)]}$$

From thesis (VI), we easily obtain the derived inference schema:

$$\text{(v)}\ \frac{U \to (V \to W)}{V \to (U \to W)}$$

(VII) $\qquad (U \to V) \to [(V \to W) \to (U \to W)]$

Proof. We simply apply inference schema (v) to thesis (V).

Thesis (VII) provides us with two more derived inference schemata:

(vi) $\dfrac{U \to V}{(V \to W) \to (U \to W)}$ and (viᵃ) $\dfrac{S \to (U \to V)}{S \to [(V \to W) \to (U \to W)]}$

ad (viᵃ)

(iv) $\dfrac{(U \to V) \to [(V \to W) \to (U \to W)]}{\{S \to (U \to V)\} \to \{S \to [(V \to W) \to (U \to W)]\}}$ [thesis (VII)]

(i) $\dfrac{S \to (U \to V)}{S \to [(V \to W) \to (U \to W)]}$ [supposition]

(3) We now have at our disposal a suitable apparatus for proving a few more theses which we shall need.

(VIII) $\qquad\qquad\qquad U \to [(U \to V) \to V]$

Proof. (v) $\dfrac{(U \to V) \to (U \to V)}{U \to [(U \to V) \to V]}$ [thesis (IV)]

(IX) $\quad (U \to V) \to [\{(U \to W) \to W\} \to \{(V \to W) \to W\}]$

Proof. We apply inference schema (viᵃ) to thesis (VII).

(X) $\quad [\{[(U \to V) \to V] \to V\} \to V] \to [(U \to V) \to V]$

Proof. (vi) $\dfrac{(U \to V) \to \{[(U \to V) \to V] \to V\}}{[\{[(U \to V) \to V] \to V\} \to V] \to [(U \to V) \to V]}$ [thesis (VIII)]

(XI) $\qquad\qquad \{(U \to V) \to V\} \to \{(V \to U) \to U\}$

Proof. [thesis (VII)]

(viᵃ) $\dfrac{\{(U \to V) \to V\} \to \{(V \to U) \to [(U \to V) \to U]\}}{\{(U \to V) \to V\} \to [\{[(U \to V) \to U] \to U\} \to \{(V \to U) \to U\}]}$
(v) $\dfrac{}{\{[(U \to V) \to U] \to U\} \to [\{(U \to V) \to V\} \to \{(V \to U) \to U\}]}$

The proof is completed by an application of *modus ponens* in connection with axiom (III). This is the first time we have applied this axiom.

(XII) $\{[\{(U \to V) \to V\} \to W] \to W\} \to \{[\{(U \to W) \to W\} \to V] \to V\}$

Proof. Let $(A) \to (B)$ be an abbreviation for the formula which we wish to establish as a thesis.

$$
\begin{array}{cl}
\text{(v)} & \dfrac{\{(U \to V) \to V\} \to \{(V \to U) \to U\} \quad \text{[thesis (XI)]}}{(V \to U) \to [\{(U \to V) \to V\} \to U]} \\[2ex]
\text{(vi}^{\text{a}}\text{)} & \dfrac{}{(V \to U) \to \{(U \to W) \to [\{(U \to V) \to V\} \to W]\}} \\[2ex]
\text{(vi}^{\text{a}}\text{)} & \dfrac{}{(V \to U) \to [\{[\{(U \to V) \to V\} \to W] \to W\} \to \{(U \to W) \to W\}]} \\[2ex]
\text{(v)} & \dfrac{}{(A) \to [(V \to U) \to \{(U \to W) \to W\}]} \\[2ex]
\text{(vi}^{\text{a}}\text{)} & \dfrac{}{(A) \to \{[\{(U \to W) \to W\} \to V] \to [(V \to U) \to V]\}} \\[2ex]
\text{(vi}^{\text{a}}\text{)} & \dfrac{}{(A) \to [\{[(V \to U) \to V] \to V\} \to (B)]} \\[2ex]
\text{(v)} & \dfrac{}{\{[(V \to U) \to V] \to V\} \to [(A) \to (B)]}
\end{array}
$$

Again the proof is completed by an application of *modus ponens* in connection with axiom (III).

(4) In connection with the above proofs it may be good to stress that in referring, for instance, to axiom (II) or to thesis (VIII), we tend to express ourselves elliptically. In stating that formula (VIII) is a thesis, we meant to imply that *every* formula $U \to [(U \to V) \to V]$ is a thesis or, still more precisely, that, *for every choice of the formulas U and V*, the corresponding formula $U \to [(U \to V) \to V]$ is a thesis. And when, in the proof of this statement, we referred to thesis (IV) we meant to imply that, *for every choice of the formula W* and hence, in particular, for every choice which would be appropriate in the context of our proof, the corresponding formula $W \to W$ must be a thesis; the relevant formula $U \to V$ then turned out to be an appropriate choice for W.

This discussion may also serve to explain the manner in which we described the axioms from which we started. We did not simply adopt three particular formulas (I)-(III); we adopted *all* formulas having certain specific shapes, characterized by what was elliptically referred to as the *axioms* (I)-(III). It is preferable, and in fact customary to refer to such expressions by the name of *axiom-schemata*.

5. COMPLETENESS

We started our discussion in Section 1 by characterizing logic as a *theory of deductive inference.* In point of fact, it seems beyond dispute that in logic we are primarily concerned with the notion of a set K of premisses U *entailing* a certain conclusion Z, or of a conclusion Z *logically following* from the premisses U in a certain set K. Both the deduction-theoretic and the semantic approach seem to be compatible with such a conception of logic, even though they start from quite divergent interpretations of the notion of entailment.

K entails Z from a deduction-theoretic point of view, if Z can be obtained from K by some adequate method of formal deduction as characterized by the requirements (i)-(iij) in Section 2, *sub* (4). As a concrete example of an adequate method of deduction we introduced the method of deduction by closed deductive tableaux. The construction of a deductive tableau for a sequent K/Z was based on the closure and reduction schemata (i), (ij^{aI}), (ij^b).

K entails Z from a semantic point of view if, whenever all premisses U in K are true under a valuation w, Z must also be true under that valuation w. In this case we found it convenient to consider more general problems of entailment, characterized by sequents K/L, K and L being arbitrary finite sets of formulas U and V. It was shown that problems of this kind (designated as valuation problems) could be solved by constructing suitable semantic tableaux. This remark suggested the notion of a fully adequate method of formal deduction, which was characterized by the requirements (i)-(v) in Section 3, *sub* (6). As a concrete example of a fully adequate method of formal deduction we introduced the method of deduction by closed semantic tableaux. The construction of a semantic tableau for a sequent K/L was based on the closure and reduction schemata (i), (ij^a), (ij^b).

As compared to the method of deductive tableaux, semantic tableaux provide us with a *stronger* method of deduction. That is, any deduction permitted by the first method can also be carried out by the second, whereas the second method makes allowance for certain deductions which the first method does not permit. We shall show, however, that nevertheless each deduction by the second method can be transformed into a certain deduction by the first method if only the set K of the premisses is suitably enlarged.

It may seem that we cannot reasonably anticipate a similar relationship between the deduction-theoretic and semantic approaches on the one hand and the axiomatic approach on the other. For the axiomatic approach does not involve the analysis of a certain connection between a set K of premisses U and a set L of conclusions V; it merely confers a certain privileged status upon a certain class of formulas, called *theses*. In view of the remarks at the end of Section 1, we may expect these theses to be identical with the *logical identities*; but thus far we have not even established this apparently rather remote connection between the axiomatic and the semantic approach.

Nevertheless we shall see that the connections are as close as could be wished.

(1) Let us consider the following fragment of a semantic tableau.

	True			False	
	K'			Z	
	$Y \rightarrow U$				
(ij^a)	$X \rightarrow V$				
	(i)	(ij)		(i)	(ij)
(ij^a)		U		Y	
	(iij)	(iv)		(iij)	(iv)
		V		X	

Now it may happen that the closure of the sequent (iij) results from the fact that the succedent of this sequent contains the formula Z. Then the corresponding deductive tableau for the given sequent $(K', Y \rightarrow U, X \rightarrow V)/Z$ will not be closed.

	Premisses			Conclusions	
	K'			Z	
	$Y \rightarrow U$				
(ij^{aI})	$X \rightarrow V$				
	(i)	(ij)		(i)	(ij)
(ij^{aI})		U		Y	Z
	(iij)	(iv)		(iij)	(iv)
		V		X	Y

For in this tableau the closure of the subordinate sequent (iij) is prevented by the fact that the formula Z is supplanted by the formulas Y and X.

However, this impediment can be overcome if to the antecedent $(K', Y \rightarrow U, X \rightarrow V)$ we add an appropriate application of Peirce's Law, namely, the formula $[(Z \rightarrow X) \rightarrow Z] \rightarrow Z$.

	Premisses		Conclusions		
	K'		Z		
	$Y \rightarrow U$				
	$X \rightarrow V$				
$(\text{ij}^{a\text{I}})$	$[(Z \rightarrow X) \rightarrow Z] \rightarrow Z$				
(i)		Z	$(Z \rightarrow X) \rightarrow Z$		Z
(ij^{b})					
$(\text{ij}^{a\text{I}})$	$Z \rightarrow X$		Z		
	(i)	(ij)	(i)		(ij)
$(\text{ij}^{a\text{I}})$		U	Y		Z
	(iij)	(iv)	(iij)	(iv)	
$(\text{ij}^{a\text{I}})$		V	X	Y	
(i)	X		Z		

The corresponding deductive tableau shows that this additional premiss enables us to have the formula X again supplanted by the formula Z. Thus the formula Z is again available for bringing about the closure of the subordinate sequent (iij).

Moreover, suppose that after using Z we should still need the formula Y in the succedent. This formula has been supplanted by X and Z, but it can be restored if to the antecedent we add still another application of Peirce's Law, namely, the formula $[(Y \rightarrow Z) \rightarrow Y] \rightarrow Y$.

It will be clear that in general if a semantic tableau for a sequent K/Z is closed, there will also be a closed deductive tableau for a certain sequent K^*/Z, where K^* results from K by the addition of certain appropriate applications of Peirce's Law. An inspection of the given closed semantic tableau for the sequent K/Z will show which applications of Peirce's Law are to be added to K and how the closed deductive tableau for the sequent K^*/Z is to be obtained.

(2) Conversely, let K/Z be any sequent and let K^* be obtained by adding

30

certain applications of Peirce's Law to the antecedent K. Then, if a certain deductive tableau for the sequent K^*/Z is closed, any semantic tableau for the sequent K/Z must also be closed. For suppose that a certain semantic tableau for the sequent K/Z is not closed. Then, by the result in Section 3, *sub* (3), this tableau provides us with a valuation w under which all premisses U in K are true whereas the conclusion Z is false. From the discussion in Section 3, *sub* (8), it follows that every application of Peirce's Law is a logical identity and hence is true under every valuation. So all premisses in K^* are true under the valuation w and Z is false. By the result in Section, 3 *sub* (3), it follows that no semantic tableau for the sequent K^*/Z can be closed. On the other hand, the given closed deductive tableau for this sequent is at the same time a closed semantic tableau. So we have refuted our supposition; therefore, any semantic tableau for the sequent K/Z must be closed.

(3) Suppose that the succedent L of a sequent K/L consists of several formulas $V_1, V_2, \ldots, V_n$. Let Z, the *representing formula* for the succedent L, be

$$((((\ldots((V_n \to V_{n-1}) \to V_{n-1}) \to \ldots) \to V_2) \to V_2) \to V_1) \to V_1.$$

Then, by reduction schema (ij^c) in Section 3, *sub* (12), the semantic tableau for the sequent K/Z reduces to that for the sequent K/L. In particular, the semantic tableau for the sequent K/L will be closed, if and only if the semantic tableau for the sequent K/Z is closed.

(4) Combining the remarks under (1)–(3), we may state:

Theorem 1. The semantic tableau for a sequent K/L will be closed, if and only if a certain deductive tableau for a sequent K^*/Z is closed, where K^* is obtained from K by adding suitable applications of Peirce's Law and Z is the representing formula for the succedent L.

(5) Let us denote as an *intuitionistic thesis* any thesis which can be proved on the basis of axioms (I) and (II) alone. Then we can introduce a certain method of formal deduction, as follows. A conclusion Z is said to be *intuitionistically deducible* from a set K of premisses if Z can be obtained from K by the following operations: (i) *modus ponens*; (ij) adding (suitably chosen) intuitionistic theses to K, or, more precisely:

31

(D1) A conclusion Z is *intuitionistically deducible* from a set K of premisses, if and only if there exists a finite sequence of formulas
$X_1, X_2, \ldots, X_k$ such that, for each j ($1 \leq j \leq k$), either X_j is an
intuitionistic thesis or a premiss in K or else we can find numbers
m and n ($1 \leq m, n < j$) such that X_n is ($X_m \to X_j$), whereas
X_k is Z. Any such sequence is denoted as an *intuitionistic deduction*
of Z from K.

(6) We now can prove:

Theorem 2. The method of formal deduction defined by (D1) is an
adequate one in accordance with requirements (i)-(iij) in Section 2.

Proof. We have to show that the above method makes allowance for the
closure and reduction schemata (i), (ij^{aI}), and (ij^b).
ad (i) The conclusion Z is clearly deducible from the set (K', Z).
ad (ij^{aI}) We have to show that, if U is deducible from $(K', U \to V)$ and
Z is deducible from $(K', U \to V, V)$, then Z is deducible from $(K', U \to V)$.
Now, on account of our supposition, we have deductions:

$$
\begin{array}{ccc}
K' & & K' \\
U \to V & \text{and} & U \to V \\
\vdots & & V \\
U & & \vdots \\
& & Z
\end{array}
$$

We clearly obtain a deduction of Z from $(K', U \to V)$ by combining the
given deductions in the manner suggested by the diagram below.

$$
\begin{array}{c}
K' \\
U \to V \\
\vdots \\
U \\
V \\
\vdots \\
Z
\end{array}
$$

ad (ij^b) We have to show that, if V is deducible from (K, U), then $U \to V$
is deducible from K. We consider two sequences of formulas.

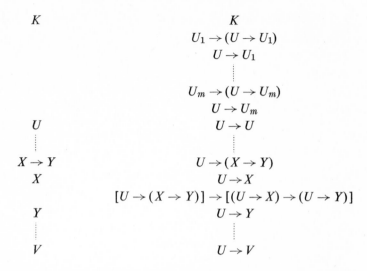

At the left side, we have the given deduction of V from (K, U). At the right side, this deduction is converted into a deduction of $U \to V$ from K. In the first place, if U_1, U_2, ... U_m are the premisses in K and the intuitionistic theses appearing in the given deduction, then we can obviously deduce the formulas $U \to U_1$, $U \to U_2$, ..., $U \to U_m$. U is not supposed to be an intuitionistic thesis, but fortunately $U \to U$ is an intuitionistic thesis in its own right. Finally, whenever in the given deduction we apply *modus ponens* to obtain Y from $X \to Y$ and X, the fact that $[U \to (X \to Y)] \to [(U \to X) \to (U \to Y)]$ is an intuitionistic thesis enables us to deduce $U \to Y$ from $U \to (X \to Y)$ and $U \to X$. Thus the sequence at the right side is an intuitionistic deduction of $U \to V$ from K. This completes our proof.

Theorem 2 is the so-called *deduction theorem* which was published independently by Herbrand and by Tarski in 1929. Church has observed that its proof involves only axioms (I) and (II).

Theorem 3. If a formula Z is intuitionistically deducible from a set K, or $(U_1, U_2, \ldots, U_m)$, then the formula Y, or:

$$U_1 \to (U_2 \to (\ldots \to (U_m \to Z) \ldots)),$$

is an intuitionistic thesis; in particular, if Z is intuitionistically deducible from the empty set $\emptyset$, then Z itself is an intuitionistic thesis.

Proof. If Z is intuitionistically deducible from K then, by the discussion of reduction schema (ij^b) in our above proof of Theorem 2, it follows that the formula Y is deducible from the empty set $\emptyset$.

Now suppose that Z is intuitionistically deducible from the empty set $\emptyset$. Then Z can be obtained by means of *modus ponens* from a certain set of intuitionistic theses; it follows that Z is itself an intuitionistic thesis.

Theorem 4. A formula Z is intuitionistically deducible from a set K if and only if a deductive tableau for the sequent K/Z is closed.

Proof. (a) Suppose we have a closed deductive tableau for the sequent K/Z. Then every adequate method of deduction enables us to deduce Z from K. Thus, by Theorem 2, Z is intuitionistically deducible from K. (b) The converse statement will not be used and, therefore, its proof (which is not simple) will be omitted.

(D2) A conclusion Z is said to be *(classically) deducible* from a set of premisses K if Z can be obtained from K by the following operations: (i) *modus ponens*, (ij) adding (suitably chosen) theses to K.

Let us denote the formula Y, described in the statement of Theorem 3, as the *representing formula* of the sequent K/Z. If the succedent L of a sequent K/L consists of several formulas, then K/L will have the same representing formula as K/Z, where Z is the representing formula of L.

Theorem 5. The method of formal deduction defined by (D2) is an adequate one in accordance with requirements (i)-(iij) in Section 2.

Proof. Only very minor changes are needed in our above proof of Theorem 2.

Theorem 6. If a formula Z is deducible from a set K, then the representing formula Y of the sequent K/Z is a thesis; in particular, if Z is deducible from the empty set $\emptyset$, then Z itself is a thesis.

Proof. No changes are needed in the proof of Theorem 3.

Theorem 7. If the semantic tableau for the sequent K/L is closed, then the representing formula Z of L is deducible from K and the representing formula Y of K/L is a thesis; in particular, if the semantic tableau for the sequent $\emptyset/Z$ is closed, then Z itself is a thesis.

34

Proof. Let the semantic tableau for the sequent K/L, where K is $(U_1, U_2, \ldots, U_m)$ and L is $(V_1, V_2, \ldots, V_n)$, be closed. Then, by Theorem 1, we can, by adding suitable applications $P_1, P_2, \ldots, P_k$, of Peirce's Law, enlarge K into a set K^* such that a certain deductive tableau for K^*/Z is closed. By Theorem 3, the representing formula:

$$P_1 \to (P_2 \to (\ldots \to (P_k \to (U_1 \to (U_2 \to (\ldots \to (U_m \to Z)\ldots))))\ldots))$$

is an intuitionistic thesis and hence a thesis. Since $P_1, P_2, \ldots, P_k$ are axioms of (classical) logic, it follows by *modus ponens* that Y is a thesis.

Since Y is a thesis, it follows that Z is (classically) deducible from K. And, if K is empty, then Z itself is a thesis.

Theorem 8. Every logical identity is a thesis.

Proof. If Z is a logical identity, then the semantic tableau for the sequent $\emptyset/Z$ must be closed. Thus by Theorem 7, Z, being its representing formula, must be a thesis.

Theorem 9. Every thesis is a logical identity.

Proof. By constructing suitable semantic tableaux, we first show that every application of the axiom-schemata (I)-(III) is a logical identity.

Secondly, we wish to prove that if both U and $U \to V$ are logical identities, then so is also V. So suppose that under a certain valuation w we have $w(V) = 0$. Since U is a logical identity, we have $w(U) = 2$. By rule (S1), it follows that $w(U \to V) = 0$. But this contradicts our supposition according to which $U \to V$ is a logical identity.

Finally, let U be an arbitrary thesis. Then there must be a certain finite sequence of formulas $X_1, X_2, \ldots, X_k$ which constitutes a proof of U as a thesis. If X_k, or U, is not a logical identity, then either it is the only formula in the sequence which is not a logical identity or else it is preceded by other formulas in the sequence which also are not logical identities. Either way there will be a *first* formula X_j in the sequence ($j = k$ or $j < k$) which is not a logical identity.

Now either X_j is an application of one of the axiom-schemata (I)-(III) or else we can find numbers m and n ($1 \leq m, n < j$) such that X_n is $X_m \to X_j$. However, since X_j is not a logical identity, it cannot be an application of an axiom-schema by our first observation. On the other hand, since X_m and X_n precede X_j, they must be logical identities. But by our second remark, if X_m and $X_m \to X_j$ are logical identities, then X_j must also be a

35

logical identity. It follows that no formula X_j as described can be found. Hence X_k, or U, must be a logical identity.

Theorem 10. Let K/L be any sequent, let Y be the representing formula of the succedent L, and let Y be the representing formula of K/L; if Z is (classically) deducible from K, or Y is a thesis, then the valuation problem expressed by K/L admits of no solution.

Proof. Let w be any valuation such that $w(U) = 2$ for every formula U in K and $w(V) = 0$ for every formula V in L. Then we have, by rule (S1), $w(Z) = w(Y) = 0$. Therefore, if Z is deducible from K or Y is a thesis, a valuation w of this kind cannot be found; in other words, the valuation problem expressed by K/L admits of no solution.

Theorem 11. The method of formal deduction defined by (D2) is a fully adequate one in accordance with requirements (i)-(v) in Section 3.

Proof. By Theorem 5, we know already that requirements (i)-(iij) are fulfilled. It follows from Theorem 10 that requirement (iv), and from Theorem 7 that requirement (v), is fulfilled.

Theorem 12. Let K/L be any sequent, let Z be the representing formula of the succedent L, and let Y be the representing formula of K/L; then exactly one of the following groups of conditions must be fulfilled, and two conditions in each group are equivalent.

(I): (i) the semantic tableau for the sequent K/L is closed; (ij) Y is a thesis; (iij) Z is deducible from K, and the deduction of Z from K can be carried out in the following manner: we first prove Y as a thesis, and we then apply *modus ponens* so as to remove the premisses $U_1, U_2, \ldots, U_m$; (iv) there is no valuation w under which all formulas U in K are true and all formulas V in L are false.

(II): (v) the semantic tableau for the sequent K/L is *not* closed; (vi) Y is not a thesis; (vij) Z is not deducible from K; (viij) there is a valuation w under which all formulas U in K are true and all formulas V in L are false.

Proof. It will be clear that either condition (i) or condition (v) must be fulfilled, and that they cannot be both fulfilled.
Moreover, condition (i) implies condition (iij) by Theorem 7; condition (iij) implies condition (ij) by Theorem 6; condition (ij) implies condition

36

(iv) by Theorem 10; and condition (iv) implies condition (i) by the discussion in Section 3, *sub* (3); *cf.* Section 33, Theorem 2ª. It follows that all conditions (i)-(iv) are equivalent; therefore, their negations, as stated under (v)-(viij) are also equivalent.

Theorem 13. For every formula Z exactly one of the following conditions must be fulfilled:

(I) Z is both a thesis and a logical identity.

(II) Z is not a thesis, and there is a valuation w under which Z is false.

Proof. We apply Theorem 12 to the special case of a sequent $\emptyset/Z$.

The Theorems 5-13 express various aspects of the fact that, on the basis of (D2), the axiomatic method provides us with a method of formal deduction which is fully adequate, that is: *adequate, sound,* and *complete,* and which, therefore, is equivalent to the method of deduction by means of closed semantic tableaux. Our proof of equivalence is *entirely constructive*: it provides us with complete instructions for converting a closed semantic tableau into a deduction as required by (D2), and conversely. It should be noted that deduction as required by (D2) makes allowance for those versions of the schemata of closure and reduction which are applied in the construction of semantic tableaux.

Being both sound and complete, any fully adequate method of formal deduction is in harmony with our intuitive conception (perhaps, rather, with our various intuitive conceptions) of *entailment*. Moreover, there is a *decision method* for (entailment or) formal deducibility, that is, a procedure which enables us for any given K and Z to find out, by a finite procedure, whether or not Z is deducible from K. This procedure consists in constructing a semantic tableau for the sequent K/Z.

To conclude, I wish to make a few remarks on the application of the above methods of deduction in the construction and development of *deductive theories*. As a basis for a deductive theory T we select a certain set K of *axioms* or *postulates* from which by and by the *theorems X, Y, Z,* ..., are deduced. However, after deducing X, we do not usually deduce Y from K alone. It is often convenient to use X as a *lemma*; this means that we either deduce Y from (K, X) or first deduce $X \rightarrow Y$ from K and then infer Y from X and $X \rightarrow Y$ by *modus ponens*. This current practice is justified by:

Theorem 14. If X is deducible from K and $X \rightarrow Y$ from (K, X), then Y is deducible from K.

Proof. Let w be any valuation under which all formulas U in K are true. Since X is deducible from K, it follows that $w(X) = 2$. Thus all formulas U in (K, X) are true under the valuation w. Since $X \rightarrow Y$ is deducible from (K, X), it follows that $w(X \rightarrow Y) = 2$. Hence, by rule (S1), we must have $w(Y) = 2$.

Now suppose Y not to be deducible from K. Then, by Theorem 12, there is a valuation w under which all formulas in K are true and Y is false; but this clearly contradicts our previous conclusion. Thus Y must be deducible from K.

CHAPTER II

FULL SENTENTIAL LOGIC

6. INTRODUCTION

The idea of a separate development of purely implicational logic seems to have originated with Alfred Tarski well before 1930; in that year a compilation of results by J. Łukasiewicz, Tarski, and a few other logicians was published. The subject was discussed later on by M. Wajsberg (1936), L. Henkin (1949), and K. Schröter (1958). The introduction of sequents, with its deduction-theoretic motivation, is due independently to G. Gentzen (1934) and to S. Jaskowski (1934); its semantic motivation seems to be original. An advancement, as compared to Gentzen's and Jaskowski's technique, seems to be the conception of their rules of inference as rules of reduction.

It may seem out of place that so much attention has been given here to a somewhat sophisticated treatment of a quite embryonic fragment of logic, and so a few words of explanation may be in order. In the first place, I feel that from the very beginning one should become acquainted with the deduction-theoretic, the semantic, and the axiomatic conception of logic; for if at first one is faced with only one of these conceptions, the result will be that later on the other conceptions will appear either less sound or more obscure, whereas logic as a whole will look artificial or at least unduly sophisticated. If, however, the three different conceptions had been presented at once in the context of a more advanced version of logic, the discussion in Chapter I would have become unnecessarily involved. Furthermore, purely implicational logic is by no means as embryonic as it seems. Relatively little has to be added if it is to be developed into such versions of logic (that is, classical logic, no systematic treatment of intuitionistic logic being attempted in this book) as provide a basis for deductive reasoning as found in mathematics and science. And as soon as the necessary supplementary elements have been introduced, we shall again profit by the rather substantial treatment of purely implicational logic in Chapter I.

In our discussion of the more advanced parts of logic we shall no longer take into account the deduction-theoretic conception. From a strictly *formalistic* point of view which is characterised by the avoidance of any reference to the *meaning* of our symbols or to the *truth* or *falsehood* of our formulas, it can be adequately replaced by the axiomatic conception of logic.

7. INTRODUCTION OF FURTHER SENTENTIAL CONNECTIVES

In this Section we shall successively introduce *disjunction, conjunction,* and *negation* which are expressed, respectively, by the symbols '∨', '&', and '⎯⎯'. In the first place, we have to expand the rules (F2) and (S1) in Section 1 as follows:

(F2) If both U and V are formulas, then $(U \to V)$, $(U \vee V)$, and $(U \& V)$ will be formulas, and if U is a formula, then $\bar{U}$ will be a formula [in practice, the outermost parentheses of compound formulas will be omitted];

(S1) If either U is false or V is true, then $U \to V$ is true, and if U is true and V is false then $U \to V$ is false; if either U or V is true, then $U \vee V$ is true, and if both U and V are false, then $U \vee V$ is false; if both U and V are true, then $U \& V$ is true, and if either U or V is false, then $U \& V$ is false; and, finally, if U is true, then $\bar{U}$ is false, and if U is false, then $\bar{U}$ is true.

Rule (F1) remains unchanged, whereas it may be left to the reader to give an appropriate restatement of rule (F3).

(1) For *disjunction* the above semantic rule suggests the following *reduction schemata.*

	True		False			True	False
	K'		L			K	L'
(iij^a)	$U \vee V$				(iij^b)		$U \vee V$
	(i)	(ij)	(i)	(ij)			U
	U	V					V

If these reduction schemata are added then, as far as formulas containing implication and disjunction are concerned, the construction of a semantic tableau constitutes, as before, a fully adequate method of deduction. It will not be necessary to repeat the discussion in Section 3.

We now observe that the formula $U \lor V$ always takes the same truth value as the formula $(U \to V) \to V$; this is perhaps most easily seen from the *'official'* truth table.

U	V	$U \to V$	$(U \to V) \to V$	$U \lor V$
0	0	2	0	0
2	0	0	2	2
0	2	2	2	2
2	2	2	2	2

Clearly from a semantical point of view $U \lor V$ could be, so to speak, *defined* as $(U \to V) \to V$.

From an axiomatic point of view, a corresponding result can be achieved as follows. In the first place we expand our set of axioms (I)–(III) so as to make allowance for the introduction of formulas U, V, and W in which disjunction appears. [Later on, when further sentential connectives or other logical notations are introduced, the corresponding expansion of the relevant set of axioms will be tacitly presupposed.] Moreover, we admit as axioms all formulas:

(IV) $(U \lor V) \to [(U \to V) \to V]$,   (V) $[(U \to V) \to V] \to (U \lor V)$,

whereas the rules (T1–3) in Section 4 remain unchanged.

(2) I wish to show that Theorems 5 ff. in Section 5 still apply if we take into account those formulas in which disjunction appears. Our first step consists in twice comparing two typical fragments of a semantic tableau.

	True	False		True		False	
		Z		$(U' \lor V') \to$ $\to [(U' \to V') \to V']$		Z	
(iij^a)	$U' \lor V'$ $U' \mid V'$		(ij^a)	$U' \lor V'$			
			(i)	$(U' \to V') \to V'$	$U' \lor V'$		
			(ij^a)				
			(ij^b)		V'	$U' \to V'$	
				U'		V'	

41

True	False		True		False
	Z		$[(U'' \to V'') \to V''] \to$		Z
	⋮		$\to (U'' \vee V'')$		⋮
	$U'' \vee V''$				$U'' \vee V''$
(iij^{b})	U''	(ij^{a})	$U'' \vee V''$	$(U'' \to V'') \to V''$	
	V''	(i) ⋯			
		(ij^{c})			U''
					V''

A comparison of the first two fragments leads to the insight that in the construction of a semantic tableau for the sequent $\emptyset/Z$ each application of reduction schema (iij^{a}) can be replaced by suitable applications of the closure and reduction schemata (i), (ij^{a}), and (ij^{b}), provided the corresponding formula:

$$(U' \vee V') \to [(U' \to V') \to V']$$

be added to the antecedent. A comparison of the other two fragments shows that, likewise, each application of reduction schema (iij^{b}) can be avoided if we add the corresponding formula:

$$[(U'' \to V'') \to V''] \to (U'' \vee V'')$$

to the antecedent. Let K/Z be the sequent which results from systematically applying this procedure.

Now suppose that Z is a logical identity. Then the semantic tableau for the sequent $\emptyset/Z$, constructed under schemata (i)-(iij), must be closed. It follows that the semantic tableau for the sequent K/Z, constructed under schemata (i) and (ij) alone, is also closed. In the construction of this last tableau, the formulas $U' \vee V'$ and $U'' \vee V''$ are not 'treated'; they behave like atoms. Thus the last tableau can be looked upon as a deduction in purely implicational logic and hence we can apply Theorem 7 with the understanding that in proving the thesis:

$$U_1 \to (U_2 \to (\ldots \to (U_m \to Z) \ldots))$$

we have to rely on the expanded version of the set of axioms (I)-(III). However, all formulas U_1, U_2, ..., U_m are applications of axiom-schemata (IV) and (V). Thus by using these axiom-schemata as well and applying *modus ponens* we can prove that Z is a thesis. It follows that at least the second part of Theorem 7 remains valid for the system of logic under consideration. Starting from this result, it is not difficult to adapt the proofs of Theorems 5–14.

(3) For *conjunction* we obviously have the *reduction schemata*:

	True	False			True	False	
	K'	L			K	L'	
	$U \& V$					$U \& V$	
(iv^a)				(iv^b)	(i) $\mid$ (ij)	(i) $\mid$ (ij)	
	U					U $\mid$ V	
	V						

It is, however, not possible to *define* conjunction in terms of implication alone and thus the problem of suitably expanding our set of axioms becomes more involved than in the case of disjunction. The following solution is due to L. Kalmar, Wajsberg, and Henkin.

If in some manner we could express within our symbolism the falsehood of a formula, then we could also express the truth of a formula and hence we could in a sense translate rule (S1) into our symbolism. Specifically, let Z be any false formula; then we can take $U \rightarrow Z$ to express the falsehood of U and $(U \rightarrow Z) \rightarrow Z$ to express its truth.

Unfortunately, there is at the present stage of development of our symbolism no formula Z which we know for certain to be false. It is easy to see that a formula Z which contains only implication must be true if all atoms $A, B, C, \ldots$ appearing in it are true; this remark also holds true for formulas Z containing, besides implication, disjunction and conjunction.

However, it is not necessary to have a formula Z which is *known* to be false; it is sufficient to have a formula Z which, in a certain context, is *assumed* to be false. And in the case in which we are interested, namely, in the deduction of a sequent $\emptyset/Z$, such a formula is readily available. Translating rule (S1) as far as it is concerned with the truth and falsehood of a formula $U \& V$, we obtain the following axioms:

(VI) $\{(U \rightarrow Z) \rightarrow Z\} \rightarrow [\{(V \rightarrow Z) \rightarrow Z\} \rightarrow \{[(U \& V) \rightarrow Z] \rightarrow Z\}]$,

(VII) $(U \rightarrow Z) \rightarrow [(U \& V) \rightarrow Z]$,

(VIII) $(V \rightarrow Z) \rightarrow [(U \& V) \rightarrow Z]$.

Actually, we could adopt simpler axioms and still adapt the proofs of Theorems 5–14; but, as we will see very soon, this point is not particularly important.

(4) Turning now to *negation*, we will clearly have the following *reduction schemata*:

	True	False			True	False
	K'	L			K	L'
	$\bar{U}$					$\bar{U}$
(vᵃ)		U		(vᵇ)	U	

'Translating' the relevant part of rule (S1) by Kalmar's and Henkin's device, we obtain the following axioms for negation:

$$\text{(IX)} \qquad [(U \to Z) \to Z] \to (\bar{U} \to Z),$$
$$\text{(X)} \qquad (U \to Z) \to [(\bar{U} \to Z) \to Z].$$

We shall, however, use instead:

$$\text{(IX)} \qquad U \to (\bar{U} \to Z),$$
$$\text{(X)} \qquad (U \to \bar{U}) \to \bar{U}.$$

Theorem 15. If we admit formulas containing both implication and negation and if to axiom-schemata (I)-(III) we add the axiom-schemata (IX) and (X), then Theorems 5–14 remain valid.

Proof. We have no trouble in extending (the statement and) the proof of Theorem 8. As to Theorem 7, we twice compare two typical fragments of a semantic tableau for the representing formula Z of a sequent K/L.

	True	False			True	False	
		Z			$U' \to (\overline{U'} \to Z)$	Z	
	$\overline{U'}$				$\overline{U'}$		
(vᵃ)		U'		(ijᵃ)	$\overline{U'} \to Z$	U'	
				(ijᵃ)			
				(i)		Z	$\overline{U'}$

True	False		True	False
	Z		$(U'' \rightarrow \overline{U''}) \rightarrow \overline{U''}$	Z
$\vdots$	$\vdots$		$\vdots$	$\vdots$
	$\overline{U''}$			$\overline{U''}$
(v^{b}) U''		(ij^{a})		
		(i) $\overline{U''}$	$U'' \rightarrow \overline{U''}$	
		(ij^{b})		
		U''		$\overline{U''}$

As under (2), we observe that the applications of schemata (v) can be replaced by applications of schemata (i) and (ij), provided we add suitable formulas $U' \rightarrow (\overline{U'} \rightarrow Z)$ and $(U'' \rightarrow \overline{U''}) \rightarrow \overline{U''}$ to the antecedent. Let $U_1, U_2, \ldots, U_m$ be all formulas added in this manner. Then clearly the semantic tableau for the sequent $\emptyset/Z$ constructed under schemata (i), (ij), and (v) will be closed, if and only if the semantic tableau for the sequent $(U_1, U_2, \ldots, U_m)/Z$ constructed under schemata (i) and (ij) alone is closed. In the second construction, the formulas $\overline{U'}$ and $\overline{U''}$ behave like atoms and hence the second tableau can be considered as a formal deduction in purely implicational logic. Then by Theorem 7 (in its original form), the formula:

$$U_1 \rightarrow (U_2 \rightarrow (\ldots \rightarrow (U_m \rightarrow Z) \ldots))$$

is a thesis of purely implicational logic. Since $U_1, U_2, \ldots, U_m$ are applications of axiom-schemata (IX) and (X), we prove by *modus ponens* that the formula Z is a *thesis of sentential logic in implication and negation*. Theorems 7 and 8 being now established for this enlarged version of sentential logic, the discussion of the remaining theorems presents no difficulties.

(5) Theorem 15 expresses the *deduction-theoretic completeness* of sentential logic in implication and negation. We shall now state and prove another theorem which expresses the *definition-theoretic completeness* (or *functional completeness*) of this version of sentential logic and so explain why this version is more important than, say, sentential logic in implication and conjunction.

Theorem 16. Let o be a sentential connective whose meaning is given

45

by a semantical rule or by a truth table. Then it is possible to find a formula $f(A, B, \ldots)$ of sentential logic in implication and negation which satisfies the following conditions:

(i) under every valuation w, $w[o(A, B, \ldots)] = w[f(A, B, \ldots)]$;

(ij) Theorem 15 will hold for sentential logic in implication, negation, and o, provided the following axiom-schemata be introduced:

$$o(U, V, \ldots) \to f(U, V, \ldots),$$
$$f(U, V, \ldots) \to o(U, V, \ldots).$$

Proof. We shall first establish the existence of a formula $f(A, B, \ldots)$ which satisfies condition (i).

(I) Suppose that o is a unary connective. Then it must have one of four truth tables which are represented in the columns (a), (b), (c) and (d) below:

	(a)	(b)	(c)	(d)
A	oA	oA	oA	oA
0	0	0	2	2
2	0	2	0	2

Accordingly we take as a formula $f(A)$, respectively: (a) $\overline{A \to A}$, (b) A, (c) $\bar{A}$, and (d) $A \to A$.

(II) Now let o be a binary connective. We consider the formula $o(A, B \to B)$. Since $w[B \to B] = 2$, $w[o(A, B \to B)]$ will depend only upon $w(A)$; therefore, we may consider $o(A, B \to B)$ to be $o_1(A)$, o_1 being a unary connective. Likewise, we may consider $o(A, \overline{B \to B})$ to be $o_2(A)$. By our result under (I), we know already that suitable formulas $f_1(A)$ and $f_2(A)$ will correspond to $o_1(A)$ and $o_2(A)$. These formulas being given, it will be clear that as a formula $f(A, B)$ we can take:

$$[f_1(A) \to \bar{B}] \to \overline{[f_2(A) \to B]}.$$

The case of a ternary connective is treated similarly. We now wish to show that the formula $f(A, B)$ under (II) also satisfies condition (ij). This is done by twice comparing two fragments of a semantic tableau; it will not be necessary to dwell upon this matter.

(6) As an application, I consider the introduction of the *equivalence*

46

or *biconditional* expressed by the symbol '↔'. We have to expand rule (F2) in a straightforward manner; furthermore, we add to rule (S1) the clause:

(S1′) If U and V are both true or both false, then $U \leftrightarrow V$ is true; if U is true and V is false or vice versa, then $U \leftrightarrow V$ is false.

As formulas $f_1(A)$ and $f_2(A)$ we may take, respectively, A and $\bar{A}$; accordingly, we may take as a formula $f(A, B)$:

$$[A \to \bar{B}] \to \overline{[\bar{A} \to B]}.$$

Therefore, the biconditional is clearly characterized by the following axiom-schemata:

(XI) $(U \leftrightarrow V) \to \{[U \to \bar{V}] \to \overline{[\bar{U} \to V]}\}$,

(XII) $\{[U \to \bar{V}] \to \overline{[\bar{U} \to V]}\} \to (U \leftrightarrow V)$.

We have the reduction schemata:

	True		False				True		False	
	K'		L				K		L'	
(ij′a)	$U \leftrightarrow V$					(ij′b)			$U \leftrightarrow V$	
	(i)	(ij)	(i)	(ij)			(i)	(ij)	(i)	(ij)
	U			U			U	V	V	U
	V			V						

CHAPTER III

THEORY OF QUANTIFICATION, EQUALITY,
AND FUNCTIONALITY

8. NOTATION

The first step in the development of a theory of quantification will be a suitable expansion of our notation. In addition to our atoms $A, B, C, \ldots$, we shall now need:

individual parameters: $a, b, c, \ldots$; arbitrary individual parameters will be denoted as $p, p', p'', \ldots$;

individual variables: $x, y, z, \ldots$; arbitrary individual variables will be denoted as $v, v', v'', \ldots$;

parameters for unary predicates (that is, for properties inherent in individual objects): $A', B', C', \ldots$;

parameters for binary predicates (that is, for relations between individual objects): $A'', B'', C'', \ldots$;

parameters for ternary predicates: $A''', B''', C''', \ldots$ [We will not explicitly deal with quaternary, ... predicates.].

In addition to the sentential connectives $\rightarrow$, $\vee$, &, and $^{\overline{}}$, we shall need *general quantifiers* (x), (y), (z), ... and *existential quantifiers* (Ex), (Ey), (Ez), ... for individual variables.

The notion of a *formula* is then characterised by the following stipulations:

(F1) All *atoms*:

$A, B, C, D, \ldots$,

$A'(a), \ A'(b), \ A'(c), \ \ldots, \ A'(p), \ \ldots, \ B'(a), \ B'(b), \ \ldots,$
$B'(p), \ \ldots, C'(a), \ \ldots, C'(p), \ \ldots,$

$A''(a, \ a), \ A''(a, \ b), \ \ldots, \ A''(b, \ a), \ \ldots, \ A''(p, \ p'), \ \ldots,$
$B''(a, a), \ \ldots, B''(p, p'), \ \ldots,$

$A'''(a, a, a), \ \ldots, A'''(p, p', p''), \ \ldots$

will be formulas;

(F2a) If both U and V are formulas, then $(U \rightarrow V)$, $(U \vee V)$, and $(U \ \& \ V)$ will be formulas; and if U is a formula, then $\bar{U}$ will be a formula;

48

(F2^b) If $U(p)$ is a formula in which the parameter p actually appears, and in which neither the variable v nor the quantifiers (v) and (Ev) appear, then $(v)U(v)$ and $(Ev)U(v)$ will be formulas; $U(v)$ is understood to result from $U(p)$ by replacing each occurrence of the parameter p by an occurrence of the variable v;

(F3) Nothing will be a formula, except on the strength of (F1) and (F2).

Expressions $V(v)$, $W(v, v')$, ..., $Z(v, v', v'', ...)$ resulting from the replacement, in formulas, of parameters p, p', p'', ..., by variables v, v', v'', ..., may present themselves as transition products in the construction of formulas and may also appear as parts of formulas, but they are not themselves considered as formulas. As a *closure* U^0 of an expression U of this kind we consider each formula $(v)(v')(v'')$ ... U obtained by suitably placing general quantifiers in front of it. If U happens to be a formula, then its closure U^0 will be U itself.

9. REDUCTION SCHEMATA

For the time being we shall restrict our discussion to those formulas in which, besides sentential connectives, only general quantifiers appear.

We shall not try here to state a suitably expanded version of our semantic rule (S1) but we will, on the strength of our 'intuitive' understanding of such phrases as: '*For every x, we have*: ...', '*For every y, we have*: ...', accept the following *reduction schemata*:

	True	False		True	False
	K'	L		K	L'
	$(v)U(v)$				$(v)U(v)$
(vi^a)	$U(p)$		(vi^b)		$U(p)$

In schema (vi^a), p may be any individual parameter appearing in K', L, or $(v)U(v)$, or, if no such parameter is available, any individual parameter. In (vi^b), however, p must be a 'fresh' parameter, that is, a parameter not yet appearing in K, L', or $(v)U(v)$, and not previously introduced under (vi^a) or (vi^b).

On the basis of reduction and closure schemata (i)-(vi), we can now

49

construct semantic tableaux for all sequents K/L such that K and L consist of formulas of the kind mentioned above.

If a semantic tableau for the sequent $\emptyset/Z$ is closed, then the formula Z will be called a *tautology* (of quantification theory).

10. AXIOMATIC METHOD

To our axioms as stated in Sections 5 and 7 we now add, as axioms for general quantification, all formulas:

(XIII) $\qquad\qquad (v)\,U(v) \to U(p)\,,$

(XIV) $\qquad\qquad (v)\,[\,\{V(v) \to (v')\,V(v')\} \to W\,] \to W\,.$

Our inference schemata will be *modus ponens* and *generalization*

$$\text{(i}^0)\frac{\begin{array}{c}U\to V\\U\end{array}}{V} \qquad\qquad \text{(i}^0)\frac{\begin{array}{c}U\\U\to V\end{array}}{V} \qquad\qquad \text{(ij}^0)\frac{U(p)}{(v)\,U(v)}$$

It will not be necessary to restate the definitions of the notion of a *thesis* (Section 4) and of the notion of (classical) *deducibility* (Section 5, *sub* (6)).

11. WEAK COMPLETENESS THEOREMS

In the first place, we prove the following variant to Theorem 8:

Theorem 17. Every tautology is a thesis.

Proof. Again we twice compare two typical fragments of a semantic tableau.

True	False		True	False
K'	Z		K'	Z
			$(v)\,U(v) \to U(p)$	
$(vi^a)\dfrac{(v)U(v)}{U(p)}$		(ij^a)	$\dfrac{(v)U(v)}{}$	
		(i)	$U(p)$	$(v)\,U(v)$

50

True	False		True	False
K	Z		K	Z
			$U(p) \to (v)U(v)$	
	$(v)U(v)$			$(v)U(v)$
(vi^b)		(ij^a)		
	$U(p)$			$(v)U(v)$ | $U(p)$
		(i)		

Essentially, we proceed in the same way as before. However, some special caution is required because of the fact that the formula:

$$U(p) \to (v)U(v)$$

is not an axiom.

Suppose Z to be a tautology. Then we have a closed semantic tableau for the sequent $\varnothing/Z$. The formulas $(v)U(v) \to U(p)$ corresponding to applications of reduction schema (vi^a) will be denoted as A-*clauses*, the formulas $U(p) \to (v)U(v)$ corresponding to those of reduction schema (vi^b) as B-*clauses*. Let $p_1, p_2, \ldots, p_n$ be an enumeration of all parameters introduced under reduction schema (vi^b) in the order of their respective introduction. Let $(v_k)U_k(v_k)$ be the formula whose appearance prompted the introduction of p_k. We construct a sequence of formulas $Z_0, Z_1, \ldots, Z_n$, as follows:

$$Z_0 \text{ will be } Z,$$
$$Z_k \text{ will be } \{U_k(p_k) \to (v_k)U_k(v_k)\} \to Z_{k-1}.$$

Now consider the formula Y, or $A_1 \to (A_2 \to (\ldots \to (A_m \to Z_n)\ldots))$, where $A_1, A_2, \ldots, A_m$ are all A-clauses taken in an arbitrary order. The formula Y is the representing formula of a sequent K^*/Z, where K^* is the set of all A- and B-clauses. It follows from the above comparison of semantic tableaux that the semantic tableau for the sequent K^*/Z is closed under schemata (i)–(v) alone. Hence, by Theorem 16, the formula Y is a thesis by purely sentential logic. Furthermore, since all A-clauses are applications of axiom-schema (XIII), m applications of *modus ponens* will show that Z_n is a thesis.

Finally, suppose that $Z_k (1 \leq k \leq n)$ is a thesis. Then we have:

$$\text{(ij}^0) \quad \frac{\{U_k(p_k) \to (v_k)U_k(v_k)\} \to Z_{k-1}}{(v_k')[\{U_k(v_k') \to (v_k)U_k(v_k)\} \to Z_{k-1}]} \quad \text{(supposition]}$$

$$\text{(i}^0) \quad \frac{(v_k')[\{U_k(v_k') \to (v_k)U_k(v_k)\} \to Z_{k-1}] \to Z_{k-1}}{Z_{k-1}} \quad \text{[axiom (XIV)]}$$

51

Thus, since Z_n is a thesis, so is also Z_{n-1}; ...; since Z_k is a thesis, so is also Z_{k-1}; ...; and, finally, since Z_1 is a thesis, so is also Z_0, or Z. This completes our proof.

As a counterpart to Theorem 7, we have:

Theorem 18. If a semantic tableau for the sequent K/Z is closed where $K = (U_1, U_2, \ldots, U_m)$, then it is possible to deduce Z from K in the following manner. We first prove that Y, or:

$$U_1 \to (U_2 \to (\ldots \to (U_m \to Z) \ldots)),$$

is a thesis; we then apply *modus ponens* so as to remove the premises $U_1, U_2, \ldots, U_m$.

Proof. Since clearly a semantic tableau for the sequent $\emptyset/Y$ is closed, it follows that Y is a tautology and hence, by Theorem 17, a thesis.

Remark. It should be noted that generalization, as an inference schema is applied, in quantification theory, only in proving a thesis. In deducing a conclusion Z from a set K of premises, the only inference schema to be applied is *modus ponens*. It follows from Theorem 18 that it is adequate for this purpose.

Theorem 19. If, by the method described in Theorem 18, X is deducible from K and $X \to Y$ from (K, X), then by the same method Y is deducible from K.

Proof. It is sufficient to show that the formula:

$$\{U_1 \to (U_2 \to (\ldots \to (U_m \to (X \to (X \to Y))) \ldots))\} \to$$
$$\to [\{U_1 \to (U_2 \to (\ldots \to (U_m \to X) \ldots))\} \to$$
$$\to \{U_1 \to (U_2 \to (\ldots \to (U_m \to Y) \ldots))\}]$$

is a thesis. Let us draw up a semantic tableau for the case $m = 2$.

True	False
$U_1 \rightarrow (U_2 \rightarrow (X \rightarrow (X \rightarrow Y)))$ $U_1 \rightarrow (U_2 \rightarrow X)$ U_1 U_2	$\{\ldots\} \rightarrow [\{\ldots\} \rightarrow \{\ldots\}]$ $\{\ldots\} \rightarrow \{\ldots\}$ $U_1 \rightarrow (U_2 \rightarrow Y)$ $U_2 \rightarrow Y$ Y

	True	False
	$U_2 \rightarrow X$	U_1
	X .	U_2
	$U_2 \rightarrow (X \rightarrow (X \rightarrow Y))$	U_1
	$X \rightarrow (X \rightarrow Y)$	U_2
	$X \rightarrow Y$	X
	Y	X

It follows that the method of deduction described in Theorem 18 makes allowance for current practice in the construction and development of deductive theories as discussed in connection with Theorem 14. For deduction by means of closed semantic tableaux we have a similar result.

Theorem 20 (Gentzen, 1934). If semantic tableaux for the sequents K/X and $(K, X)/X \rightarrow Y$ are closed, then there is also a closed semantic tableau for the sequent K/Y.

Proof. The proof is given in the *Appendix*, Section 36; *cf.* p. 69. Theorem 27.

Theorem 21 (J. Herbrand, 1930). Every thesis is a tautology.

Proof. In the first place we show by constructing semantic tableaux that all applications of our axiom-schemata are tautologies. The case of axiom-schema (XIV) requires some special attention.
The construction starts as follows.

	True	False
		$(v)[\{V(v) \to (v')V(v')\} \to W] \to W$
(ijᵇ)	$(v)[\{V(v) \to (v')V(v')\} \to W]$	W
(viᵃ)	$\{V(p) \to (v')V(v')\} \to W$	
(ijᵃ)		
(i)	W	$V(p) \to (v')V(v')$
(ijᵇ)	$V(p)$	$(v')V(v')$
(viᵇ)		$V(p')$

At this point some doubts may arise as to the final success of the construction. However, if we apply once again reduction schema (viᵃ) with the new parameter p', then $V(p')$ will appear in the left column and thus the closure schema can be applied.

Secondly, we have to show: if the inference schemata (i⁰) and (ij⁰) are applied to tautologies, then the formulas which result are again tautologies.

ad (i⁰) Suppose that U and $U \to V$ are tautologies. Then we have closed semantic tableaux for the sequents $\emptyset/U$ and $\emptyset/U \to V$; it clearly follows that there is also a closed semantic tableau for the sequent $U/U \to V$. Therefore, by Theorem 20 there is a closed semantic tableau for the sequent $\emptyset/V$, so V is a tautology.

ad (ij⁰) Suppose that $U(p)$ is a tautology; then we have a closed semantic tableau for the sequent $\emptyset/U(p)$. In constructing a semantic tableau for the sequent $\emptyset/(v)U(v)$ we shall of course start by applying reduction schema (viᵇ) so as to obtain $U(p)$ in the right column. From this point on we simply duplicate the given semantic tableau for the sequent $\emptyset/U(p)$.

Theorem 22. A semantic tableau for a sequent K/L is closed if and only if the representing formula Z of L is deducible from K by the method described in Theorem 18.

Proof. By Theorem 18, the closure of a semantic tableau for K/L implies the deducibility of Z from K. Now suppose Z to be deducible from K by the method described in Theorem 18. Then clearly the representing formula Y of K/L is a thesis and hence, by Theorem 21, a tautology. Therefore, the semantic tableau for the sequent $\emptyset/Y$ must be closed and hence the semantic tableau for the sequent K/L as well.

54

(1) Let us now turn to *existential quantification* which is, in the present context, characterised by the following *reduction schemata*:

	True	False		True	False
	K'	L		K	L'
(vij^a)	$(Ev)U(v)$		(vij^b)		$(Ev)U(v)$
	$U(p)$				$U(p)$

In (vij^a), p must be a 'fresh' parameter; in (vij^b), p is either a parameter appearing in K' (K), L (L'), or $(Ev)U(v)$, or, if no such parameter is available, any parameter.

Existential quantification is clearly definable in terms of general quantification and negation. Therefore, we may adopt as *axioms for existential quantification* all formulas:

(XV) $$(Ev)U(v) \rightarrow \overline{(v)\,\overline{\overline{U(v)}}}\,,$$

(XVI) $$\overline{(v)\,\overline{U(v)}} \rightarrow (Ev)U(v)\,.$$

The notion of a tautology can easily be expanded so as to make allowance for formulas involving existential quantification. Then we will clearly have:

Theorem 23. If we admit formulas containing implication, negation (and eventually, other sentential connectives), general quantification and existential quantification, and if we adopt all axiom-schemata (I)–(XVI), then Theorems 17–22 remain valid.

(2) The conception of Theorems 17–23 as expressing completeness (if only in a weakened sense) is, of course, suggested by their partial analogy to the completeness theorems in Section 5. This conception will receive further support from a comparison with the stronger completeness theorems which we shall establish in Chapter IV.

12. EQUALITY

In applications of formal logic in the methodology of a deductive discipline T we usually deal with deduction problems K/Z where K is the set of all specific axioms for T and where Z is a theorem (or supposed theorem) of T. The individual variables x, y, z, ..., are then taken to range over a specific set S, for instance, the set of all natural numbers. The predicate parameters A, B, ..., which occur in K are taken to stand for the specific notions $\mathbf{A}$, $\mathbf{B}$, ..., of the deductive discipline T.

(1) There is one notion which appears in practically every deductive discipline, namely, the binary predicate which is usually represented by the symbol '$=$' and denoted as *equality* (or *identity*). Because of its omnipresence it seems natural to consider equality a notion which like implication or general quantification belongs to formal logic rather than to the various deductive disciplines in which it happens to appear.
On the other hand, it is sometimes felt that such a conception is incompatible with the fact that equality is often closely connected with other notions which must undoubtedly be considered peculiar to certain deductive disciplines. This dilemma is sometimes solved by making a distinction between *identity* as a purely logical notion and *equality* as being specifically of mathematical disciplines; however, from such a procedure new complications arise.
We shall not go further into this discussion which nevertheless may serve to illustrate our observation that, whenever equality appears in a deductive discipline T, the development of T will involve two groups of axioms concerning equality, namely:
 (i) axioms valid in every deductive discipline in which equality appears;
 (ij) axioms which are peculiar to T.

(2) It seems practical to consider the axioms under (i) *logical axioms* and to extend the system of elementary logic in a manner such as to include these axioms.
In order to do so we add to the symbols mentioned in Section 8 the binary predicate parameter $=$ and, accordingly, we restate rule (F1) so as to make allowance for the introduction of the atoms:

$$a = a, a = b, \ldots, b = a, \ldots, p = p', \ldots .$$

In addition, we introduce the following *axioms for equality*:

(XVII) $\qquad\qquad\qquad (x)[x = x]\,,$

(XVIII) $\qquad\qquad\qquad (x)(y)[x = y \to y = x]\,,$

(XIX) $\qquad\qquad (x)(y)(z)[\{x = y\ \&\ y = z\} \to x = z]\,,$

as well as an infinite sequence of *axiom-schemata for extensionality*:

(XX) $(x)(y)[x = y \to \{A'(x) \to A'(y)\}]$,

and similarly for B', C', D', $\ldots$;

$$(x)(y)(z)[x = y \to \{[A''(x, z) \to A''(y, z)] \,\&\, [A''(z, x) \to A''(z, y)]\}],$$

and similarly for B'', C'', $\ldots$;

$$(x)(y)(z)(u)[x = y \to$$
$$\to \{[A'''(x, z, u) \to A'''(y, z, u)] \,\&\,$$
$$\&\, [A'''(z, x, u) \to A'''(z, y, u)] \,\&\,$$
$$\&\, [A'''(z, u, x) \to A'''(z, u, y)]\}];$$

and similarly for B''', $\ldots$, etc.

(3) In the development of a deductive discipline T, the above equality and extensionality axioms are applied in the following manner. Let K be the set of all specific axioms of T; we list those predicate parameters which appear in K. We then add to K the axioms (XVII)–(XIX) as well as those applications of axiom-schemata (XX) which correspond to these predicate parameters.

Let K^* be the set of axioms thus obtained; then the theorems of T will be deduced from K^* by one of the two methods referred to in Theorem 22.

To give an example, let us suppose that K consists of the formula $(x)A(x, x)$ and that we wish to deduce the formula:

$$(y)(z)[y = z \to A(y, z)].$$

We construct the following closed semantic tableau.

	True	False
	(1) $(x)A(x, x)$	(2) $(y)(z)[y = z \to A(y, z)]$
	(3) $(x)[x = x]$	
	(4)–(5) (XVIII)–(XIX)	
	(6) $(x)(y)(z)[x = y \to$	
	$\to \{[A(x, z) \to A(y, z)]\,\&$	
	$\&\,[A(z, x) \to A(z, y)]\}$	
(vi^b)		
(ij^b)		(7) $a = b \to A(a, b)$
(vi^a)	(8) $a = b$	(9) $A(a, b)$
(vi^a)	(10) $A(a, a)$	
	(11) $a = b \to$	
	$\to \{[A(a, a) \to A(b, a)]\,\&$	
	$\&\,[A(a, a) \to A(a, b)]\}$	
(ij^a)		
(i)	(13) $[\ldots]\,\&\,[\ldots]$	(12) $a = b$
(iv^a)		
	(14) $A(a, a) \to A(b, a)$	
(ij^a)	(15) $A(a, a) \to A(a, b)$	
(i)	(17) $A(a, b)$	(16) $A(a, a)$

13. FUNCTIONALITY

Let $A(x, y, z)$ refer to a ternary predicate **A** such that, for any values a and b given to x and y, there is *exactly one* value c of z for which $A(a, b, c)$ holds true. Then we say that $A(x, y, z)$ defines z as a *function* of x and y and we write $z = f(x, y)$. We wish to expand our symbolism so as to make allowance for this notation.

We do so by introducing *parameters for individual constants* $h, h', h'', \ldots,$ *parameters for unary functions* $g, g', g'', \ldots,$ *parameters for binary functions* $f, f', f'', \ldots,$ and so on. We restate rule (F1) so as to admit atoms:

$$h = a, h = b, \ldots, h = p, \ldots, h' = a, \ldots,$$
$$g(a) = a, g(a) = b, \ldots, g(a) = p, \ldots, g(b) = a, \ldots,$$
$$g(p) = p', \ldots, g'(a) = a, \ldots,$$
$$f(a, a) = a, f(a, a) = b, \ldots, f(a, a) = p, \ldots,$$
$$f(p, p') = p'', \ldots, f'(a, a) = a, \ldots\,.$$

Furthermore, we express the specific purpose of this new notation by introducing the following *axioms of functionality*:

(XXI) $$(Ex)(t)[h = t \leftrightarrow t = x],$$
$$(x)(Ey)(t)[g(x) = t \leftrightarrow t = y],$$
$$(x)(y)(Ez)(t)[f(x, y) = t \leftrightarrow t = z],$$

and similarly for h', h'', $\ldots$, g', g'', $\ldots$, f', f'', $\ldots$.
In the development of a deductive discipline T these axioms are used in the same manner as the axioms for equality and extensionality.

(1) Now suppose that from a certain set K we can deduce a certain formula $(x)(y)(Ez) U(x, y, z)$. We replace K by the set $K' =$

$$= (K, (x)(y)(Ez) U(x, y, z)).$$

Then, by Theorem 20, a formula Z will be deducible from K' if and only if it is deducible from K.
Let f be a binary function parameter which does not appear in K; we now replace the set K' by the set $K'' =$

$$= (K, (x)(y)(z)[f(x, y) = z \rightarrow U(x, y, z)]).$$

A formula Z *which does not contain the function parameter* f will be deducible from K'' if and only if it is deducible from K'. This can be seen from a comparison of two suitable semantic tableaux; see below.
Thirdly, let us replace K'' by $K^0 =$

$$= (K, (x)(y) U(x, y, f(x, y))),$$

with the understanding that, if we apply reduction schema (vi^a) with respect to the formula $(x)(y) U(x, y, f(x, y))$, the '*term*' $f(p, p')$ which results shall be used in the same manner as an individual parameter. A formula Z as above will again be deducible from K^0 if and only if it is deducible from K and from K''. I now give typical fragments from the semantic tableaux corresponding to the deduction problems K'/Z, K''/Z, and K^0/Z.

True	False
K	Z

$(vi^a)\dfrac{(x)(y)(Ez)\,U(x,y,z)}{(Ez)\,U(p,p',z)}$

$(vij^a)\dfrac{}{U(p,p',p'')}$

True	False
K	Z

$(x)[x=x]$

$(x)(y)(z)[f(x,y)=z \to$
$\to U(x,y,z)]$

$(x)(y)(Ez)(t)[f(x,y)=t \leftrightarrow$
$\leftrightarrow t=z]$

(vi^a)
$(vij^a)\dfrac{}{(Ez)(t)[f(p,p')=t \leftrightarrow t=z]}$

$(vi^a)\dfrac{}{(t)[f(p,p')=t \leftrightarrow t=p'']}$

$(vi^a)\dfrac{}{f(p,p')=p'' \leftrightarrow p''=p''}$

$(ij^{a'})\dfrac{}{p''=p''}$

True			False
$f(p,p')=p''$			$f(p,p')=p''$
$p''=p''$			$p''=p''$

(i)

(vi^a)
$(ij^a)\dfrac{}{f(p,p')=p'' \to U(p,p',p'')}$

(i)

	True	False
	$U(p,\ p',\ p'')$	$f(p,p')=p''$

True	False
K	Z

$(vi^a)\dfrac{(x)(y)\,U(x,y,f(x,y))}{U(p,p',f(p,p'))}$

It will be clear that, after all, the net contribution of the formulas $(x)(y)(Ez)\,U(x, y, z)$, $(x)(y)(z)[f(x, y) = z \to U(x, y, z)]$, and $(x)(y)\,U(x, y, f(x, y))$ to the closure of the three tableaux is the same. Thus we have:

Theorem 24. Let the formula $(x)(y)(Ez)\,U(x, y, z)$ be deducible from a set

K, let f be a function parameter which does not appear in K, let K'' and K^0 be obtained by adding to K, respectively, the formulas:

$$(x)(y)(z)[f(x, y) = z \rightarrow U(x, y, z)],$$

and:

$$(x)(y) U(x, y, f(x, y)),$$

and let Z be a formula in which the parameter f does not appear. Then Z will be deducible from K'' and from K^0 if and only if it is deducible from K. In particular, K'' and K^0 will be formally consistent if and only if K is formally consistent.

The case in which $U(x, y, z)$ is a formula $(t)\{V(x, y, t) \leftrightarrow z = t\}$ is of particular importance.

Theorem 25. Let the formula $(x)(y)(Ez)(t)\{V(x, y, t) \leftrightarrow z = t\}$ be deducible from a set K, let f be a function parameter which does not appear in K, let K^0 be obtained by adding to K the formula:

$$(x)(y)(t)[V(x, y, t) \leftrightarrow f(x, y) = t],$$

and let Z be a formula in which the parameter f does not appear. Then Z will be deducible from K^0 if and only if it is deducible from K. In particular, K^0 will be formally consistent if and only if K is formally consistent.

A few words may be added to explain significance of Theorem 25. The formula $(x)(y)(Ez)(t)\{V(x,y,t) \leftrightarrow z = t\}$ expresses the fact that there is, for every x and y, exactly one z which, taken as a value of t, satisfies the condition $V(x, y, t)$. We usually express this fact by saying that *z is a function of x and y* and it is a current practice to indicate this more explicitly by introducing a new function symbol f and by writing $f(x, y)$ instead of z; the formula $(x)(y)(t)[V(x, y, t) \leftrightarrow f(x, y) = t]$ is taken to *define* the function f. Theorem 25 makes it clear that to this practice no objection can be made since it produces no contradictions and, as far as formulas in the original notation (without f) are concerned, no new theorems.

61

CHAPTER IV

COMPLETENESS OF ELEMENTARY LOGIC

14. INTRODUCTION

The introduction of the notion of a *tautology* in Section 9 must be understood as a provisory measure prompted by considerations which I shall now explain.

The results in Section 5, and in particular Theorem 12, were based upon the distinction made in Section 3 between two alternative possibilities (I) and (II). The construction of a semantic tableau must after a finite number of steps produce either possibility (I) or possibility (II). Each of these two possible cases could be further analysed by means of purely finitistic methods. For elementary logic, the situation is more involved since, because of the introduction of 'fresh' individual parameters under the reduction schemata (vi^b) and (vij^a), the construction of a semantic tableau may lead to an *infinite regress*.

Of course it may happen that, in a finite number of steps, the construction produces a closed semantic tableau. In that case, we have a situation which is very similar to the above possibility (I) and which admits likewise of an analysis by means of finitistic methods. The notion of a tautology was introduced with a view to duplicating as far as possible the discussion in Section 5. In this connection, it may be recalled that the introduction of the reduction schemata (vi) and (vij) was not based on an expanded version of our semantic rule (S1). However, we shall accept no such expanded version unless it makes allowance for these reduction schemata. Therefore, if an acceptable expanded version of rule (S1) is given and if the notion of a logical identity is expanded accordingly, then every tautology as defined in Section 9 will become a logical identity; it does not follow, however, that every logical identity must be a tautology.

Owing to the possibility of an infinite regress in the construction of a semantic tableau, the alternative to the closure of a semantic tableau is *not*, in general, a straightforward counterpart to the above possibility (II). In particular, it cannot be adequately analysed by means of purely finitistic methods. Therefore, we shall now devote to this alternative a separate discussion in which infinitistic methods will be freely used.

(2) As an example, I consider the semantic tableau for the sequent $(x)(Ey)[A(x, y) \rightarrow A(y, y)]/(z)A(z, z)$.

	True		False	
(vi^b)	$(x)(Ey)[A(x, y) \rightarrow A(y, y)]$		$(z)A(z, z)$	
(vi^a)			$A(a, a)$	
(vij^a)	$(Ey)[A(a, y) \rightarrow (Ay, y)]$			
(ij^a)	$A(a, b) \rightarrow A(b, b)$			
(vi^a)		$A(b, b)$	$A(a, b)$	
(vij^a)	$(Ey)[\ldots]$	$(Ey)[\ldots]$		
(ij^a)	$A(b, c) \rightarrow A(c, c)$	$A(b, c) \rightarrow A(c, c)$		
	$\mid A(c, c) \mid$	$\mid A(c, c) \mid A(b, c) \mid$		$A(b, c) \mid$

In this case, it is easy to see that the construction can be continued indefinitely.

15. QUANTIFICATION THEORY

In order to simplify the study of infinite tableau constructions at least to some extent, we replace our individual parameters a, b, c, ... by numerals 1^*, 2^*, 3^*, ... [We use the asterisk $*$ in order to stress the distinction between the *numeral* k^* and the *natural number* k which it normally denotes. Numerals k^* are understood to serve a threefold purpose: (i) normally the numeral k^* denotes the natural number k; (ij) a numeral k^* may also play the role of a parameter having no fixed denotatum; (iij) finally the numeral k^* may be construed as a parameter which in a certain context has been given a fixed denotatum $w(k^*)$. This last situation presents itself in Section 16, *sub* (1); *cf.* Section 39.] It is also convenient to replace each formula $(Ev)U(v)$ by $\overline{(v)\overline{U(v)}}$; we then have to take into account only general quantification. Moreover, we introduce a certain function s which with each natural number k associates a natural number $s(k)$. We first arrange all formulas $(v)U(v)$ in an infinite sequence:

$$(v_1)U_1(v_1), \quad (v_2)U_2(v_2), \quad (v_3)U_3(v_3), \quad \ldots, \quad (v_k)U_k(v_k), \quad \ldots.$$

63

Because previously a formula could contain parameters, we have now to take into account the possible appearance of numerals in a formula $(v) U(v)$. The function s is determined as follows.

(A) $s(1)$ will be the smallest natural number which exceeds both 1 and all natural numbers j such that the numeral j^* appears in $(v_1) U_1(v_1)$.

(B) Suppose that the value $s(n)$ has already been found; then $s(n + 1)$ will be the smallest natural number which exceeds both $s(n)$ and all natural numbers j such that the numeral j^* appears in $(v_{n+1}) U_{n+1}(v_{n+1})$.

(1) The function s will be used in the following manner. An application of reduction schema (vi^b) originally required the introduction of a 'fresh' individual parameter p; we shall now construe the schema to require the introduction of a 'fresh' numeral k^*. And we specify once for all which particular numeral is to be chosen; if an application of reduction schema (vi^b) is prompted by the appearance of the formula $(v_n) U_n(v_n)$, then the 'fresh' numeral to be introduced will be $s^*(n)$.

(2) We do not specify the ordering of the formulas $(v) U(v)$ from which we start. Theoretically, this order is supposed to be established once for all, but practically it is much more convenient to adapt it to the particular case with which we are dealing. In the case of our above illustration, we suppose the sequence of formulas to start as follows:

$$(x)(Ey)[A(x, y) \to A(y, y)], \quad \text{hence } s(1) = 2,$$
$$(z)A(z, z), \quad \text{hence } s(2) = 3,$$
$$(y)\overline{[A(3, y) \to A(y, y)]}, \quad \text{hence } s(3) = 4,$$
$$(y)\overline{[A(4, y) \to A(y, y)]}, \quad \text{hence } s(4) = 5, \ldots.$$

Accordingly, our semantic tableau will now look as follows:

True		False	
$(x)(Ey)[A(x, y) \rightarrow A(y, y)]$		$(z)A(z, z)$	
		$A(3, 3)$	
$(Ey)[A(3, y) \rightarrow A(y, y)]$			
		$(y)\overline{[A(3, y) \rightarrow A(y, y)]}$	
		$\overline{A(3, 4) \rightarrow A(4, 4)}$	
$A(3, 4) \rightarrow A(4, 4)$			
	$A(4, 4)$	$A(3, 4)$	
$(Ey)[\ldots]$	$(Ey)[\ldots]$		
$\ldots$	$\ldots$	$\ldots$	$\ldots$
$A(4, 5) \rightarrow A(5, 5)$	$A(4, 5) \rightarrow A(5, 5)$		
$A(5, 5)$	$A(5, 5)$	$A(4, 5)$	$A(4, 5)$

Throughout the following discussion we shall suppose that the formulas in the sets K and L contain no numerals. In order to deal with a situation in which this condition is not fulfilled, it would be necessary to adapt the construction of the function s in the following manner: $s(1)$ is the smallest natural number which exceeds both 1 and all natural numbers j such that j^* appears either in K, L, or $(v_1) U_1(v_1)$.

(3) We are now equipped for a general discussion of the results which may arise from the construction of a semantic tableau for a sequent K/L. As in Section 3, *sub* (1), two cases (I) and (II) can be distinguished.

Case (I) has been discussed in Section 11; according to Theorem 18, if a semantic tableau for the sequent K/L is closed, then the representing formula Y of K/L is a thesis of quantification theory. Once a closure has been achieved, it clearly does not matter if all possibilities of applying the reduction schemata have been exhausted; the order in which the formulas have been 'treated' is also of no importance.

In case (II) however, it is clearly essential that all possibilities be exhausted and, because of the possibility of an infinite regress, this implies the necessity of applying the reduction schemata in an orderly manner so as not to miss any opportunity to achieve a closure. Such an orderly procedure is guaranteed, for instance, by the following stipulations.

(a) The formulas in K and L are numbered; the new formulas arising from the application of the reduction schemata are numbered in accordance with their relative order of appearance.

(b) This numbering determines the order in which the formulas are 'treated'. In an application of reduction schema (vi^a) we use only those numerals $k*$ which already appear in the relevant subtableau; if no numeral appears, we use the numeral 1*.

(c) Whenever under reduction schema (vi^b) a 'fresh' numeral $k*$ is introduced, we adjust all previous applications of reduction schema (vi^a).

(d) Whenever a new formula appears, the relevant subtableau is scanned for a possible closure.

If in spite of all these precautions no closure is achieved, we may be sure that no closure is possible and thus we are in case (II). However, various subcases must be distinguished.

(II^a) The completed tableau contains only finitely many formulas; in this case clearly at least one subtableau is not closed.

(II^b) The completed tableau contains infinitely many formulas but only finitely many splittings; again the tableau consists of finitely many subtableaux at least one of which contains infinitely many formulas and thus cannot be closed.

(II^c) The completed tableau contains at least one infinite string of 'nested' subtableaux in which no closure arises.

In cases (II^b) and (II^c), the closure of the tableau is not achieved because the construction leads to an *"infinite regress"*, as mentioned in Section 14. Let us select, accordingly, a subtableau or a string of 'nested' subtableaux in which no closure arises. This provides us with two (finite or infinite) lists of formulas bearing, respectively, the headings 'True' and 'False'. The first list starts with the formulas in K, the second with the formulas in L. In the case of our illustration, there are infinitely many such strings which may start, for instance, as follows.

True	False	True	False
$(x)(Ey)[\ldots]$	$(z)A(z, z)$	$(x)(Ey)[\ldots]$	$(z)A(z, z)$
	$A(3, 3)$		$A(3, 3)$
$(Ey)[\ldots]$		$(Ey)[\ldots]$	
	$(y)[\ldots]$		$(y)[\ldots]$
	$A(3, 4) \to A(4, 4)$		$A(3, 4) \to A(4, 4)$
$A(3, 4) \to A(4, 4)$		$A(3, 4) \to A(4, 4)$	
	$A(3, 4)$	$A(4, 4)$	
$(Ey)[\ldots]$		$(Ey)[\ldots]$	
$\ldots$		$\ldots$	
$A(4, 5) \to A(5, 5)$		$A(4, 5) \to A(5, 5)$	
	$A(4, 5)$	$A(5, 5)$	

(4) To fix the ideas, suppose that the formulas in K and in L contain a binary predicate parameter A and a unary predicate parameter B. Then no other predicate parameters can appear in the formulas on the list. In addition these formulas contain at least one numeral k^*. No formula can appear on both lists since in that case a closure would have arisen.

In terms of the given lists, we define a certain set S, a binary predicate (or relation) A, and a unary predicate (or property) B, as follows.

(S) The set S consists of those natural numbers k such that k^* appears in some formula on one of the lists.

(A) The binary predicate A holds between the elements j and k of S (or the element j is in the relation A to the element k) if and only if the formula $A(j^*, k^*)$ appears under the heading 'True'.

(B) The unary predicate B holds for the element j of S (or the element j has the property B) if and only if the formula $B(j^*)$ appears under the heading 'True'.

(5) So far, we have taken into account only the 'typographical' structure of the formulas on the lists. We shall now provide them with a definite *meaning* in terms of the following *hermeneutics* which is in accordance with our 'intuitive' understanding as referred to in Section 9. As usual, the numerals k^* are taken to stand for (or to serve as names of) the corresponding natural numbers k. Likewise, the parameters A and B are taken, respectively, to stand for the above predicates A and B. The formulas $A(j^*, k^*)$ and $B(j^*)$ are taken, respectively, to express the

meaning that the predicate **A** holds between j and k and that the predicate **B** holds for j. The variables $x, y, z, \ldots$, are understood to *range* over the set **S**, that is, to take the elements of **S** as values. Thus the quantifier (x) shall mean: '*for every element x of* **S** $\ldots$'; similarly for $(y), (z), \ldots$ and for $(Ex), (Ey), (Ez), \ldots$.

On account of this hermeneutics, the formulas which appear on the two lists can now be understood as expressing certain properties of the predicates **A** and **B** and of certain elements of **S**. On the basis of this understanding, we can make the following statement:

All formulas under the heading 'True' *are true and all formulas under the heading* 'False' *are false.*

Proof. Let us denote a formula as *wrongly placed* if it appears under the heading 'True' but is false, or appears under the heading 'False' but is true. Then we have to show: no formula on the two lists is *wrongly placed*. We proceed as in Section 3, *sub* (3); we restrict ourselves to discussing the most important cases.

(i) Suppose the formula $(y)X(y)$ to be wrongly placed under the heading 'True'. Then that formula must be false and hence some formula $X(k^*)$ [k in **S**] must be false. On the other hand, owing to the obligatory applications of reduction schema (vi^a), *all* formulas $X(k^*)$ must appear under the heading 'True'. Thus, if such a formula $X(k^*)$ is false, then it is wrongly placed.

(ij) Suppose $(y)X(y)$ to be wrongly placed under the heading 'False'. Suppose this formula appears in the above sequence as $(v_m) U_m(v_m)$. Then, owing to the obligatory application of reduction schema (vi^b), the formula $U_m(s^*(m))$ must also appear under the heading 'False'. On the other hand, since $(y)X(y)$ is true and since $s(m)$ is in **S**, the formula $X(s^*(m))$, or $U_m(s^*(m))$, must be true and hence it must be wrongly placed.

(iij) Suppose $\bar{X}$ to be wrongly placed under the heading 'True'. Then $\bar{X}$ must be false, and hence X must be true whereas, owing to an application of reduction schema (v^a), X must appear under the heading 'False'. Hence X is wrongly placed.

(iv) As in Section 3, *sub* (3), we may conclude that if a compound formula is wrongly placed then some atom must be wrongly placed. Thus suppose $A(j^*, k^*)$ to be wrongly placed under the heading 'False'. Then $A(j^*, k^*)$ must be true, that is, the element j must be in the relation **A** to the element k. And this is only the case of the formula $A(j^*, k^*)$ appears under the heading 'True'. But the appearance of a formula on both lists would bring about a closure. The remaining cases are treated similarly and thus the above statement may be considered as justified. We have in particular:

All formulas in K are true and all formulas in L are false.

(6) An assemblage $< S, A, B >$ of a non-empty set S and of predicates A and B defined in S is called a *structure* [of course, if the formulas in K and in L should contain still other predicate parameters $C, D, \ldots$, then we would have to consider structures involving additional predicates $C, D, \ldots$]. If with respect to such a structure a formula U or all formulas U in a set K are true, then the structure is said to provide a *model* for U or for K, respectively.

If, in addition, a formula Z or all formulas V in a set L are false, then the structure is said to provide a *counterexample* to the sequent K/Z or K/L, respectively. And if no counterexample to the sequent $\emptyset/Z$ can be found, then the formula Z is denoted as a *logical identity*. In other words, Z is a logical identity, if and only if every appropriate structure is a model for Z, that is, if Z is true with respect to every structure involving suitable predicates.

The result of our discussion under (3)–(5) can be stated as follows:

Whenever, in constructing a semantic tableau for a sequent K/L, we find ourselves in case (II), *the tableau provides a counterexample* $< S, A, B, \ldots >$ *to the sequent K/L.*

We have conversely:

If for a sequent K/L we are in case (I), *then no counterexample to the sequent K/L can be found.*

For the construction of a semantic tableau for a sequent K/L may be considered as a systematic attempt to construct a counterexample. By the closure of the tableau we discover that no such attempt can be successful. It clearly follows that there is no counterexample.

(7) We can now round off the results achieved in Section 11 by stating the following *strong completeness theorems*.

Theorem 26. Every logical identity is a tautology and therefore a thesis.

69

Proof. Let Z be a logical identity. Then there is no counterexample to the sequent $\emptyset/Z$ and therefore the semantic tableau for that sequent must be closed. So Z is a tautology and hence, by Theorem 17, a thesis.

Theorem 27. Every thesis is a logical identity and therefore a tautology.

Proof. We now complete the proof of Theorem 21. Suppose that U and $U \rightarrow V$ are logical identities whereas V is not. Then there is a counterexample to the sequent $\emptyset/V$. Now if with respect to that structure U is true, then $U \rightarrow V$ is false, hence $U \rightarrow V$ is not a logical identity; and if U is false, then U itself is not a logical identity. Both conclusions contradict our supposition. – Note that this proof is not finitistic; a finitistic proof is given in Section 36.

Theorem 28. For every sequent K/L exactly one of the following conditions must be fulfilled.
  (I) It is possible to deduce the representing formula Z of L from K in the manner described in Theorem 18.
  (II) There is a counterexample to the sequent K/L.

Proof. According as for the semantic tableau for the sequent K/L we have case (I) or case (II), condition (I) or condition (II) will be fulfilled.

Theorem 29. A set K admits of a model if and only if it is formally consistent.

Proof. We consider the sequent $K/\emptyset$ and apply Theorem 28.
ad (I) If the semantic tableau for the sequent $K/\emptyset$ is closed, then the semantic tableau for K/Z will clearly be closed for any choice of Z; so any conclusion Z is deducible from K, hence K is formally inconsistent.
ad (II) A counterexample to the sequent $K/\emptyset$ is clearly a model for the set K.

Theorem 30. A formula Z is deducible from a set K if and only if every model of K is also a model of Z.

Proof. First suppose that the semantic tableau for the sequent K/Z is closed. Then by Theorem 18, Z is deducible from K. Moreover, there is no counterexample to the sequent K/Z and thus every model of K must be a model of Z.
Secondly, suppose that the semantic tableau for the sequent K/Z is not

closed. Then this sequent admits of a counterexample and this structure is a model of K without being a model of Z. Moreover, the representing formula Y of K/Z is not a thesis and so Z cannot be deducible from K.

16. THEORY OF EQUALITY AND FUNCTIONALITY

Let us just try to apply the method of Section 15 to a problem from the theory of equality. We consider the sequent $(Ex)[x = x]/(x)(Ey)[\overline{x = y}]$ and construct a semantic tableau for it. As explained in Section 12, *sub* (3), we add to the antecedent the equality axioms (XVII)–(XIX).

	True	False
	$(Ex)[x = x]$ (XVII) $(x)(y)[x = y \rightarrow y = x]$ (XIX)	$(x)(Ey)[\overline{x = y}]$
(vijᵃ)	$1 = 1$	
(viᵇ)		
(vijᵇ)		$(Ey)[\overline{2 = y}]$
		$\overline{2 = 1}$
		$\overline{2 = 2}$
(ivᵇ)	$2 = 1$ $2 = 2$	
(viᵃ)		
(ijᵃ)	$2 = 1 \rightarrow 1 = 2$	
	$1 = 2$	$2 = 1$
(i)		

It is easy to see that further application of reduction schemata is of no avail. So we may expect the tableau to produce a certain structure $< S, A >$ which can serve as a counterexample to the given sequent. And it is easy to see how such a structure can be obtained from the tableau. The set S will consist of the two natural numbers 1 and 2 and A will be the relation which each of these two numbers has both to itself and to the other one. In the tableau this relation is represented by the symbol '$=$' and it has the properties expressed by the formulas in the antecedent without having the property expressed by the formula in the succedent. Neverthe-

71

less, this counterexample is not fully satisfactory because the relation expressed by the symbol '=' is *not* the equality relation in the set $\{1, 2\}$. In order to make up for this deficiency, we should, in some way eliminate the distinction between the elements of S. One manner to do this consists in giving a different meaning to the symbols involved. Let '1' denote, as previously, the natural number 1, let '2' denote the same natural number and let '=' denote the equality relation. If S is the set which contains only the natural number 1, then under this new hermeneutics all formulas under the heading 'True' become true and all formulas under the heading 'False' become false.

(1) Let us now turn to a more general case. Suppose we have a sequent K/L, the formulas of which may contain a binary predicate parameter A, a unary predicate parameter B, and the equality symbol. We add to the antecedent K the relevant equality and extensionality axioms (XVII)–(XX) and we construct a semantic tableau for the sequent K^*/L taking all the precautions discussed in Section 15. Suppose the semantic tableau is not closed; we select a subtableau or a string of 'nested' subtableaux in which no closure arises and thus we have again two (finite or infinite) lists of formulas bearing, respectively, the headings 'True' and 'False'. The first list starts with the formulas in K^*, the second with the formulas in L. We introduce the following hermeneutics.

(I) Each numeral k^* which appears on the lists is taken to denote a certain natural number $w(k^*)$, namely, the *smallest* natural number j such that the formula $k^* = j^*$ appears under the heading 'True'.

(II) Furthermore:

(S) the set S consists of all natural numbers $w(k^*)$,

(A) the binary predicate A holds between elements j and k of S if and only if the formula $A(j^*, k^*)$ appears under the heading 'True',

(B) the unary predicate B holds for the element j of S if and only if the formula $B(j^*)$ appears under the heading 'True',

(=) the equality symbol '=' is taken to stand for the identity of elements of S.

(2) We have to show that under this hermeneutics:
All formulas under the heading 'True' *are true, and all formulas under the heading* 'False' *are false.*

Proof. In the present case, we are in particular concerned with the atoms. ad $(=)$ Suppose that the atom $j^* = k^*$ appears under the heading 'True'. The numerals j^* and k^* denote certain natural numbers $w(j^*)$ and $w(k^*)$ in S and the equality symbol is taken to express their identity. Thus the atom $j^* = k^*$ will be true if and only if $w(j^*)$ is the same natural number as $w(k^*)$. Now consider the following fragment of our semantic tableau.

True	False
$j^* = k^*$	
$j^* = k^* \to k^* = j^*$	
$\quad\quad\quad\quad k^* = j^*$	$j^* = k^*$
$j^* = p^*$	
$(k^* = j^* \,\&\, j^* = p^*) \to k^* = p^*$	
$\quad\quad\quad\quad k^* = p^*$	$k^* = j^* \,\&\, j^* = p^*$
	$k^* = j^*$ $\mid$ $j^* = p^*$

It will be clear that, whenever $j^* = p^*$ appears under the heading 'True', so does also $k^* = p^*$, and conversely. Now $w(j^*)$ is the smallest of all these numbers p; but since $w(k^*)$ is the smallest of the same numbers p, $w(j^*)$ is the same number as $w(k^*)$. The case of a formula $j^* = k^*$ under the heading 'False' is treated similarly.

ad (B) Suppose that the atom $B(j^*)$ appears under the heading 'False'. This formula will be false if the predicate **B** does not hold for the number $w(j^*)$, that is, if the formula $B(w(j^*))$ does not appear under the heading 'True'. We consider again a suitable fragment of our semantic tableau.

True	False
	$B(j^*)$
$j^* = w^*(j^*)$	
$j^* = w^*(j^*) \to w^*(j^*) = j^*$	
$\quad\quad\quad\quad w^*(j^*) = j^*$	$j^* = w^*(j^*)$
$w^*(j^*) = j^* \to \{B(w^*(j^*)) \to B(j^*)\}$	
$\quad\quad B(w^*(j^*)) \to B(j^*)$	$w^*(j^*) = j^*$
$\quad\quad\quad\quad B(j^*)$	$B(w^*(j^*))$

If the formula $B(w^*(j^*))$ should appear under the heading 'True', then a closure would arise in the subtableau which we consider and this would contradict our supposition. So $B(w^*(j^*))$ cannot appear under the heading 'True' and hence $w(j^*)$ cannot have the property **B**. It follows that under the hermeneutics which we have adopted the formula $B(j^*)$ is false. The case of a formula $B(j^*)$ under the heading 'True' and the two cases concerning a formula $A(j^*, k^*)$ are treated similarly.

ad (S) In order to show that the set **S** is non-empty, we first observe that owing to the presence of axiom (XVII) in K^* at least one formula $k^* = k^*$ appears under the heading 'True'. Thus, if no other formula $k^* = p^*$ appears under that heading, we have $w(k^*) = k$ and hence k will be in **S**. Otherwise, we may have $w(k^*) < k$ and then $w(k^*)$ will be in **S**.

So we have proved our above statement, and we can now duplicate the discussion in Section 15, *sub* (6)–(7). Therefore:

Theorem 31. The Theorems 26–30 for elementary logic hold as well for elementary logic with equality.

(3) We now consider the case of a sequent K/L involving, besides equality, certain function parameters. To fix the ideas, let us suppose we have a binary predicate parameter A, a unary predicate parameter B, and a binary function parameter f. By adding to K the axioms (XVII)–(XIX) as well as the relevant applications of axiom-schemata (XX) and (XXI), we obtain a set K^*. If we consider $f(p, p') = p''$ as another notation for $F(p, p', p'')$, then we are in a position to apply Theorem 31. Thus, if the semantic tableau for the sequent K^*/L is not closed, there will be a counter-example $< \mathbf{S}, \mathbf{A}, \mathbf{B}, \mathbf{F} >$, where $\mathbf{F}$ is a ternary predicate. For the structure $< \mathbf{S}, \mathbf{A}, \mathbf{B}, \mathbf{F} >$, all formulas in K^* are true whereas all formulas in L are false.

Now K^* contains the formula:

$$(x)(y)(Ez)(t)([f(x, y) = t \leftrightarrow t = z]$$

which in constructing the counter-example has been treated as:

$$(x)(y)(Ez)(t)[F(x, y, t) \leftrightarrow t = z] .$$

74

This formula is true for the structure $< \mathbf{S}, \mathbf{A}, \mathbf{B}, \mathbf{F} >$. Now let $w(j^*)$ and $w(k^*)$ be any elements of $\mathbf{S}$; then the formula:

$$(Ez)(t)[F(j^*, k^*, t) \leftrightarrow t = z]$$

must be true for our structure. Hence $\mathbf{S}$ must contain a certain element $w(l^*)$ such that the formula:

$$(t)[F(j^*, k^*, t) \leftrightarrow t = l^*]$$

is true. But this clearly means that $w(l^*)$ must be the *only* element in $\mathbf{S}$ which fulfils the condition $F(j^*, k^*, t)$. Thus, since for any $w(j^*)$ and $w(k^*)$ in $\mathbf{S}$ such a unique element $w(l^*)$ in $\mathbf{S}$ can be found, it will be proper to write $w(l^*) = \mathbf{f}(w(j^*), w(k^*))$. Therefore, the function parameter f can be said to be represented in our counter-example not merely by a ternary predicate $\mathbf{F}$ but, more appropriately, by a binary function $\mathbf{f}$. So we denote our structure as $< \mathbf{S}, \mathbf{A}, \mathbf{B}, \mathbf{f} >$ and we have:

Theorem 32. The Theorems 26–30 for elementary logic hold as well for elementary logic with equality and functionality.

CHAPTER V

THE FORMALIZATION OF ARITHMETIC
AND ITS LIMITATIONS

17. AN AXIOM SYSTEM FOR ARITHMETIC

We now construct an axiom system A for arithmetic or, rather, for that part of elementary arithmetic which is concerned with the addition, multiplication, and exponentiation of natural numbers 0, 1, 2, 3, ... Although the scope of this axiomatization is rather narrow, we shall find that in a sense it encompasses a larger part of arithmetic than could have been anticipated. In addition, we shall find that there is a more or less uniform method for extending A whenever the need for a larger scope should arise. [In this respect the character of the system A is related to that of purely implicational logic.]

(1) As *terms*, we accept:
  (i) an individual constant 0, and the individual parameters $a, b, c, \ldots$;
  (ij) (St), whenever t is a term;
  (iij) $(t + t')$, $(t \cdot t')$, and $(t^{t'})$, whenever t and t' are terms.
In writing terms, we shall omit parentheses in accordance with current usage in arithmetic and algebra.
As *atoms*, we accept all expressions $t = t'$; compound formulas are constructed in accordance with the stipulations (F2) and (F3) in Section 8.

(2) We borrow our method of deduction from elementary logic with equality and terms as described in the *Appendix*, Section 37. It shall be understood that 0 is treated as h, Sx as $g(x)$, and $x + y$, $x \cdot y$ and x^y as $f(x, y)$.

(3) As *axioms* for A, we adopt:

(A1)	$(x)(y)[Sx = Sy \to x = y]$,
(A2)	$(x)[x + 0 = x]$,
(A3)	$(x)(y)[x + Sy = S(x + y)]$,
(A4)	$(x)[x \cdot 0 = 0]$,

(A5)	$(x)(y)[x \cdot Sy = x \cdot y + x]$,
(A6)	$(x)[x^0 = S0]$,
(A7)	$(x)(y)[x^{Sy} = x^y \cdot x]$,
(A8)	$(x)[\overline{0 = Sx}]$,
(A9)	$(x)[x = 0 \lor (Ey)\{x = Sy\}]$.

In accordance with the characterization of elementary logic with equality and terms in Section 37, we assume in addition the equality and extensionality axioms (XVII)–(XX).

(4) The terms:

$$0, S0, SS0, SSS0, \ldots, S[k - 2 \text{ symbols } S] S0, \ldots$$

are called *numerals* and denoted, respectively, as 0^0, 1^0, 2^0, 3^0, $\ldots$, k^0, $\ldots$. An arbitrary term t which contains no individual parameters is called a *numerical term*. If t is a numerical term and k^0 is a numeral, then the formula:

$$t = k^0$$

is called an *evaluation*.

(5) On the basis of our 'intuitive' understanding of arithmetic, we now introduce the following *hermeneutics* for numerals, numerical terms, and evaluations. We assign to each numeral and, more generally, to each numerical term t, a *numerical value* $w(t)$; with each evaluation $t = k^0$ a *truth value* $w(t = k^0)$ is associated.

(i) For $k = 0, 1, 2, 3, \ldots, w(k^0) = k$.

(ij) $w(0)$ shall be *zero* [in agreement with (i)].

(iij) $w(St)$ shall be $w(t)$ *plus one* [if t, and hence St, happen to be numerals, this is in agreement with (i)].

(iv) $w(t + t')$, $w(t \cdot t')$, and $w(t^{t'})$ shall be, respectively, *the sum of $w(t)$ and $w(t')$*, the *product of $w(t)$ and $w(t')$*, and $w(t)$ *to the power $w(t')$*.

(v) If $w(t)$ is the same number as $w(k^0)$, then $w(t = k^0) = 2$; and if $w(t)$ differs from $w(k^0)$, then $w(t = k^0) = 0$.

As an example, let us compute $w(SS0^{SS0} = SS0)$:

$$w(SS0^{SS0}) = w(SS0)^{w(SS0)} = 2^2 = 4; \quad w(SS0) = 2;$$

therefore, since $4 \neq 2$, we have $w(SS0^{SS0} = SS0) = 0$.

77

Remark. It is not difficult to see that $w(k^0)$ can be computed on the basis of clauses (ij) and (iij) alone; thus clause (i) is redundant.

Theorem 33. Let t be any numerical term. Then we can find a unique natural number k such that $w(t = k^0) = 2$ and such that $t = k^0$ is deducible in A; and if $m \neq k$, then $\overline{t = m^0}$ is deducible in A.

Proof. See *Appendix*, Section 41.

Theorem 34. The formula $S0 = 0$ is not provable in A; therefore, the deductive system A is formally consistent.

Proof. See *Appendix*, Section 41.

(6) According to Theorem 33, the deductive system A enables us to deduce each *true*, and to refute each *false*, evaluation; and according to Theorem 34, it does not permit us to deduce any false, or to refute any true, evaluation. Thus we may consider the system A as an adequate basis for *numerical computation with natural numbers* insofar as addition, multiplication, and exponentiation are involved.

But still other forms of numerical computation can be based on the system A. This will be pretty clear for subtraction and division which, in the framework of this system, can be defined as follows:

$$(x)(y)(z) [x - y = z \leftrightarrow (t) \{y + t = x \leftrightarrow t = z\}],$$
$$(x)(y)(z) [x : y = z \leftrightarrow (t) \{y \cdot t = x \leftrightarrow t = z\}].$$

The formulas $k^0 - l^0 = m^0$ and $k^0 : l^0 = m^0$ can be deduced in A whenever they are true and refuted in A whenever they are false. For this reason, these formulas may be denoted as *evaluations in the wider sense*.

We shall see in Section 18, *sub* (9) and (10) that, as far as numerical computation is concerned, the scope of the system A is considerably larger than might have been anticipated.

18. SYNTACTIC INCOMPLETENESS

I shall now have to explain, by way of introduction, a few results from elementary arithmetic which will be applied later on.

(1) We first observe that each natural number M admits of a unique representation as:

$$2^{m_1} + 2^{m_2} + \ldots + 2^{m_k} + \ldots + 2^{m_n} \quad (m_1 > m_2 \ldots > m_k > \ldots > m_n) .$$

(i) That at least one representation of this kind can be found is seen as follows. Let 2^{m_1} be the largest power of 2 which is $\leq M$; take $M_1 = M - 2^{m_1}$ and let 2^{m_2} be the largest power of 2 which is $\leq M_1$; and so on. It will be clear that in this manner a finite sequence of suitable exponents $m_1, m_2, \ldots, m_k, \ldots, m_n$ will be found.

(ij) Suppose we had still another similar representation of M as:

$$2^{p_1} + 2^{p_2} + \ldots + 2^{p_k} + \ldots \quad (p_1 > p_2 > \ldots > p_k > \ldots) ,$$

where $p_1 = m_1, p_2 = m_2, \ldots, p_{k-1} = m_{k-1}$, but $p_k \neq m_k$. Now m_k was taken as large as possible, so $p_k < m_k$, and hence $p_k \leq m_k - 1$. It follows that:

$$2^{p_k} + \ldots \leq 2^{p_k} + 2^{p_{k-1}} + 2^{p_{k-2}} + \ldots + 1 = 2^{p_k+1} - 1 < 2^{m_k} ,$$

which is clearly impossible. Thus the above representation is unique.

(2) Conversely, let any finite set $\{m_1, m_2, \ldots, m_k, \ldots, m_n\}$ of natural numbers be given (the order in which the numbers appear does not matter, but no number may appear twice); then this set is uniquely characterized by the natural number M, or:

$$2^{m_1} + 2^{m_2} + \ldots + 2^{m_k} + \ldots + 2^{m_n} .$$

(3) Finally, let a finite sequence:

$$a_1, a_2, \ldots, a_k, \ldots, a_n ,$$

of natural numbers be given. This sequence (*with* the given order of its terms!) is uniquely characterized by the finite set:

$$\{5^n, 3 \cdot 5^{a_1}, 3^2 \cdot 5^{a_2}, \ldots, 3^k \cdot 5^{a_k}, \ldots, 3^n \cdot 5^{a_n}\} .$$

This set, as we have seen under (2), can be uniquely characterized by one single natural number A. Clearly, this number A also characterizes the given finite sequence; it will be denoted as the *representing number* of the sequence.

(4) If, on the other hand, the representing number z of a finite sequence is given, then the condition for a number x to be the yth term ($y = 1, 2, 3, \ldots$) in this sequence can be stated as follows:

If z is divided by $2^{3^y \cdot 5^x}$, then the quotient is an odd number.

Therefore, if we write u for the quotient and v for the remainder, and if we introduce the definitions:

$$1 = S0, \quad 2 = SS0, \quad 3 = SSS0, \quad 5 = SSSSS0,$$

$$(x)(y)[x < y \leftrightarrow (Ez)\{x + Sz = y\}],$$

then this condition can be restated as follows in the notation of the deductive system A:

$$(u)(v)[\{z = u \cdot 2^{3^y \cdot 5^x} + v \ \& \ v < 2^{3^y \cdot 5^x}\} \to (Ew)\{u = 2 \cdot w + 1\}].$$

For this expression, we introduce the abbreviation $[z]_y = x$. The expression $[z]_0 = x$ clearly expresses the condition that for a finite sequence whose representing number is z, the sequence consists of exactly x terms. If in the expression $[z]_y = x$ the variables x, y, and z are replaced, respectively, by the numerals a^0, k^0, and A^0, then we obtain a formula $[A^0]_{k^0} = a^0$ for which we can prove: if the formula $[A^0]_{k^0} = a^0$ is true, then it is deducible in A, and if it is false, then its negation is deducible in A. Because Theorem 33 can be extended to formulas $[A^0]_{k^0} = a^0$, these formulas may be considered as *evaluations in the wider sense*.

(5) As an example, we consider the well-known arithmetical function:

$$n! = n \cdot (n - 1) \cdot (n - 2). \ldots . 3 \cdot 2 \cdot 1,$$

which is usually defined by the 'inductive' conditions:

$$1! = 1, \quad (n + 1)! = (n + 1) \cdot n!$$

We wish to restate the condition $x! = y$ in the notation of the deductive system A.

So we consider the finite sequence of the numbers:

$$1!, \quad 2!, \quad \ldots, \quad u!, \quad \ldots, \quad x!,$$

and its representing number z. This sequence is fully characterized by the following properties:

(i) It consists of x terms;

(ij) Its first term is 1;

(iij) If $0 < u < x$, then its $(u + 1)^{st}$ term is $u + 1$ times its uth term;

(iv) Its xth, and last, term is y.

It is not difficult to formulate the corresponding properties of the representing number z; as a result, the condition $x! = y$ is restated as follows:

$$(Ez)\{[z]_0 = x \ \& \ [z]_1 = 1 \ \& \ (u)(v)[(0 < u \ \& \ u < x \ \& \ [z]_u = v) \rightarrow$$
$$\rightarrow [z]_{Su} = Su \cdot v] \ \& \ [z]_x = y\} \ .$$

Again, if for the variables x and y we substitute definite numerals n^0 and m^0, either the resulting formula or its negation will be deducible in A, according as that formula is true or false, that is, according as $n! = m$ or $n! \neq m$. Thus the resulting formula may be considered as an *evaluation in the wider sense*.

(6) Aristotle had already observed, although somewhat reluctantly, a certain similarity between logical deduction and arithmetical computation. We shall now see that there is a very close similarity indeed. Specifically, let us consider the construction of purely implicational logic, as discussed in Sections 4 and 5.

In order to establish a connection between purely implicational logic and arithmetic, we associate with each formula U a natural number $g(U)$, which is called its *Gödel number* and determined by the following stipulations:

(G1) The Gödel numbers of the atoms A, B, C, ... are, respectively,
$g(A) = 7, g(B) = 7^2, g(C) = 7^3, \ldots$;

(G2) If $g(U) = u, g(V) = v$, then $g(U \rightarrow V) = 11^u \cdot 13^v$.

The introduction of Gödel numbers enables us to state the following arithmetical variant to stipulation (F3″) in Section 1:

The natural number g is the Gödel number of a formula of purely implicational logic if and only if there is a finite sequence of natural numbers $g_1, g_2, \ldots, g_k$ such that, for each j $(1 \leq j \leq k)$, there either is a natural number h such that $g_j = 7^h$ or else we can find natural numbers m and n $(1 \leq m, n < j)$ such that $g_j = 11^{g_m} \cdot 13^{g_n}$, whereas $g_k = g$.

The condition for a natural number g to be the Gödel number of a thesis of purely implicational logic can be stated similarly provided we give first a more precise statement of stipulation (T3) in Section 4; for instance:

(T3″) The formula U is a thesis of purely implicational logic if and only if there exists a finite sequence of formulas $U_1, U_2, \ldots, U_k$ such that, for each j ($1 \leq j \leq k$), either we can find formulas X, Y, Z such that U_j is $X \to (Y \to X)$ or $[X \to (Y \to Z)] \to [(X \to Y) \to (X \to Z)]$ or $[(X \to Y) \to X] \to X$ or else we can find numbers m and n ($1 \leq m, n < j$) such that U_n is $(U_m \to U_j)$, whereas U_k is U.

It is left to the reader to state a suitable arithmetical variant.

(7) Stating the condition for a natural number g to be the Gödel number of a logical identity demands somewhat more deliberation. In particular, we have to characterize the notion of a valuation but we may take advantage of the fact that, in the present context, only *partial valuations* are involved. For if U is a given formula, $w(U)$ depends only upon the truth values $w(U_j)$ assigned to the formulas U_j in (F3″). Moreover, the function w is replaced by the finite sequence of the *ordered couples* $< U_j, w_j >$, where $w_j = w(U_j)$. We thus obtain:

(S1″) A partial valuation w for a formula U is a finite sequence of ordered couples $< U_1, w_1 >, < U_2, w_2 >, \ldots, < U_k, w_k >$ where U_1, $U_2, \ldots, U_k$ are as in (F3″) whereas, in addition: (i) if U_m is the same formula as U_n, then $w_m = w_n$, (ij) if U_j is an atom, then w_j is either 0 or 2, (iij) if U_j is $(U_m \to U_n)$, $w_m = 2$, and $w_n = 0$, then $w_j = 0$, whereas (iv) if $w_m = 0$ or $w_n = 2$, then $w_j = 2$. If every sequence of this kind terminates with the ordered couple $< U, 2 >$, then U is a logical identity.

Let us replace each ordered couple $< U_j, w_j >$ by the natural number $f_j = 17^{g(U_j)} \cdot 19^{w_j}$ by which it is uniquely characterized. Then we obtain the following arithmetical variant to the stipulation (S″):

The natural number g is the Gödel number of a logical identity if and only if it is the Gödel number of a formula and if, moreover, for every finite sequence of natural numbers $f_1, f_2, \ldots, f_k$ such that: (i) for any m and n ($1 \leq m, n \leq k$), if $f_m = 17^{g'} \cdot 19^{w'}$, $f_n = 17^{g''} \cdot 19^{w''}$, $g' = g''$, then $w' = w''$; (ij) for each j ($1 \leq j \leq k$), either (ij^a) there are natural numbers h and w such that $f_j = 17^{7^h} \cdot 19^w$, $w = 0$ or $w = 2$, or (ij^b) there are natural numbers m, n ($1 \leq m, n < j$), g^0, g', g'', w^0, w', w'' such that $f_j = 17^{g^0} \cdot 19^{w^0}$, $f_m = 17^{g'} \cdot 19^{w'}$, $f_n = 17^{g''} \cdot 19^{w''}$, $g^0 = 11^{g'} \cdot 13^{g''}$,

82

whereas, if $w' = 2$ and $w'' = 0$ then $w^0 = 0$, and if $w' = 0$ or $w'' = 2$ then $w^0 = 2$, we have for any g' and w': if $f_k = 17^{g'} \cdot 19^{w'}$ and $g' = g$, then $w' = 2$.

(8) Using the device explained under (3)–(5) we can now formulate the condition for a natural number x to be the Gödel number of a formula of purely implicational logic by means of the following expression in the notation of our system A:

$$(Ez)(Ey)\{[z]_0 = y \ \& \ (s)[(1 \leqq s \ \& \ s \leqq y) \to \{(Et)([z]_s = 7^{st}) \ \vee$$
$$\vee \ (Eu)(Ev)(1 \leqq u \ \& \ 1 \leqq v \ \& \ u < s \ \& \ v < s \ \&$$
$$\& \ [z]_s = 11^{[z]_u} \cdot 13^{[z]_v})\}] \ \& \ [z]_y = x\}.$$

Let us adopt *Form*(x) as an abbreviation for this expression. In a similar manner, we can formulate the conditions for a natural number x to be the Gödel number of a thesis and to be the Gödel number of a logical identity by means of expressions in the notation of the system A; we adopt *Ths*(x) and *Logid*(x) as abbreviations for these expressions.

(9) If the variable x is replaced by a numeral k^0, then the formulas *Form*(k^0), *Ths*(k^0), and *Logid*(k^0) which result are again deducible in A or refutable in A according as they are true or false; thus these formulas may be considered as *evaluations in the wider sense* [*cf. Appendix,* Section 41].

(10) Now let us consider, instead of the relatively simple case of purely implicational logic, the more involved case presented by the deductive system A. Then we can, nevertheless, in a completely analogous manner, after introducing Gödel numbers for the (terms, expressions, and) formulas of A, state the conditions for a natural number x to be the Gödel number of a formula, of an axiom, or of a theorem of A. Using again the device explained under (3)–(5), we can formulate these conditions by means of expressions in the notation of the system A itself; let *Form*(x), *Ax*(x), and *Thm*(x) be, respectively, adopted as abbreviations for these expressions.

The formulas *Form*(k^0) and *Ax*(k^0) can still be considered as *evaluations in the wider sense*. We shall see, however, that for the formulas *Thm*(k^0) the situation is not quite so simple.

(11) Besides A, we shall consider other deductive systems B which we shall not specify but about which we shall make the following assumptions.
  (I) B is an *extension* of A both as to notation and as to provability; that is, B contains all symbols, terms, and formulas of A, but may contain additional ones; and all theorems of A are theorems of B, but B may contain additional theorems;
  (II) B is amenable to (a suitable adaptation of) the construction discussed under (6)–(10);
  (III) B is consistent.

(12) A number-theoretic predicate P is said to be *definable* in B, if there is an expression $U(x)$ of B such that the formula $U(k^0)$ is true or false according as the predicate P belongs to k or not (Tarski). In particular, the predicates expressed by *Form, Ax,* and *Thm,* as discussed under (10), are definable in A and so is also the predicate expressed by Thm_B, as discussed under (15).

(13) A number-theoretic predicate P is said to be *numeralwise represent-able* in B, if there is an expression $U(x)$ of B such that the formula $U(k^0)$ or the formula $\overline{U(k^0)}$ is a theorem of B according as the predicate P belongs to k or not (S. C. Kleene). The predicates expressed by *Form* and *Ax* are numeralwise representable in A but, as we shall see under (18), the predicates expressed by *Thm* and by Thm_B are not. In point of fact, we shall see that, even though a certain formula $Thm_B(k^0)$ is false, its negation cannot be provable in A.

Remark. Although we may be inclined to consider the notions introduced under (12) and (13) as practically equipollent, it is easy to understand that in the absence of further specifications concerning a system B it will be necessary to keep them apart. For, on the one hand, it may happen that a predicate P is definable in B by a certain expression $U(x)$ even though it is not numeralwise represented by this expression because the axioms of B are too weak to make provision for the proofs of the relevant formulas $U(k^0)$ and $\overline{U(k^0)}$. On the other hand, it may happen that there is a formula $U(x)$ of B which contains certain symbols with which no interpretation has been connected; if nevertheless the axioms of B make provision for the proofs of the appropriate formulas $U(k^0)$ and $\overline{U(k^0)}$, then $U(x)$ may numeralwise represent a predicate P without properly defining it.

(14) A number-theoretic predicate P is said to be *effectively decidable* if it admits of a *decision procedure*, that is, a mechanical device which permits us to find, in a finite number of steps, the correct answer to the question as to whether or not the predicate P belongs to a given natural number m.

(15) At this point the following observation is in order. Let U be any formula of the system B, and let g be its Gödel number. Then the construction explained under (6)–(8) provides us with a certain formula $Thm_B(g^0)$ in the notation of A which we may take to express the provability of U in B although, in accordance with the hermeneutics set forth in Section 17, *sub* (5), it is primarily an arithmetical statement which asserts the existence of a certain natural number G, namely, of the representing number of a finite sequence $g_1, g_2, \ldots, g_n (= g)$, where $g_1, g_2, \ldots, g_n$ are the Gödel numbers of certain formulas $U_1, U_2, \ldots, U_n$ (or U) which, in this order, constitute a proof of U as a theorem of B.

Now suppose that U actually is a theorem of B. Then we have a proof of U and thus we can effectively compute, first the relevant Gödel numbers $g_1, g_2, \ldots, g_n$, and then the corresponding representing number G. Thus the truth of $Thm_B(g^0)$ is merely a matter of numerical computation and hence, by Theorem 33, $Thm_B(g^0)$ is deducible in A and also in B.

The above method also permits the construction of a formula NC_B which expresses the consistency of the system B.

(16) According to *Church's thesis*, a predicate P is numeralwise representable in A [and hence in every extension B of A] if and only if it is effectively decidable. [In particular, the predicate expressed by Thm_B cannot be decidable unless it is numeralwise representable in A.] One cannot reasonably demand a proof of this thesis, since the notion of effective decidability is meant to be taken, in this context, in its '*intuitive*' sense. Nevertheless, it obtains strong support from the following considerations.

(i) Suppose the predicate P to be numeralwise represented in a system B by an expression $U(x)$. Then it can be said to be effectively decidable since we may accept as decision procedure a systematic effort to deduce in B either $U(m^0)$ or $\overline{U(m^0)}$ by constructing simultaneously and side by side the two relevant semantic tableaux. For we know in advance that, after a finite number of steps, either of the two constructions must prove successful.

(ij) Suppose we have a mechanic device which permits us to find, in a finite number of steps, the correct answer to the question as to whether or not the predicate P belongs to m. This device may involve an algorithm, an abacus, a digital computer, or what not. At any rate, the successive stages in each application of the device can be characterized by *'lines'* (or *'strings of signs'*). It is perhaps best to think of such a line as a record of the steps which, at a certain moment, have been completed.

Each step in the procedure is uniquely determined by the preceding steps and can be accounted for by writing a new line; this line results from copying the preceding line and adding the record of the last step. The first line will presumably give the number m in some special notation, say:

$$m^*$$

The last line will present a full record of the procedure, say:

$$m^* \quad \text{——} \quad \text{——} \quad r^*$$

where r may be 2 or 0 according as P belongs to m or not.

Now we may once for all associate with each line which may present itself in an application of the given device a certain Gödel number. The condition for an application of the device to provide an affirmative reply to the question as to whether or not the predicate P belongs to m can then again be stated in the familiar form:

There is a finite sequence of natural numbers $g_1, g_2, \ldots, g_p$, *such that* $g_1 = m, \ldots,$ *whereas* $g_p = 2$;

$g_2, \ldots, g_{p-1}$ are the Gödel numbers of the successive lines. As before, the method explained under (6)–(8) permits us to restate this condition in the notation of the system A. The expression $P(x)$ which results will numeralwise represent the predicate P in the system A and hence also in each of its extensions B.

(iij) From the discussion under (i) and (ij) it follows conversely that whenever a predicate P is numeralwise representable in an extension B of A, it is also numeralwise representable in the system A itself.

(17) In an entirely analogous manner, a number-theoretic function f is said to be *definable* in B, if there is an expression $U(y, x)$ of B such that the formula $U(n^0, m^0)$ is true or false according as $n = f(m)$ or not, and to be *numeralwise representable* in B, if there is an expression $U(y, x)$ of B such that $U(n^0, m^0)$ is deducible or refutable in B according as $n = f(m)$ or not.

The function f is said to be *effectively computable*, if there is a mechanical device which permits us to find, in a finite number of steps, the value $f(m)$ of the function for any given value of the argument m.

According to Church's thesis, a function f is numeralwise representable in a system A or B if and only if it is effectively computable. The discussion under (16), (i)–(iij) applies as well to this case. If the function f is numeralwise represented in B by the expression $U(y, x)$ we accept as an effective method of computing $f(m)$ a systematic effort to prove in B a formula $U(0, m^0)$, $U(S0, m^0)$, ..., $U(n^0, m^0)$, ... [for instance, let $T_0, T_1, T_2, T_3, \ldots$ be the relevant semantic tableaux; then our first step may consist in writing down the first line of T_0; our second step, in writing down the second line of T_0 and the first line of T_1; our third step, in writing down the third line of T_0, the second line of T_1, and the first line of T_2; and so on]; for we know in advance that for some n, namely, $f(m)$, a proof must result.

(18) Let us now define a number-theoretic function f_B, as follows: *We shall have $f_B(m) = n$ if either*: (i) *there are a natural number p and a formula $(x)(y) U(y, x)$ of B such that m is the Gödel number of $(x)(y) U(y, x)$, so that*

$$(y)[U(y, m^0) \leftrightarrow y = p^0]$$

is provable in B, and such that $n = p + 1$, or: (ij) *there is no natural number and no formula as described under* (i)*, and $n = 0$.*

By the method explained under (6)–(8) we can restate the above definition in the notation of the system B. The expression $F_B(y, x)$ which results defines the function f_B in the system B. Let g be the Gödel number of the formula $(x)(y) F_B(y, x)$.

We wish to compute $f_B(g)$. It will be clear that, in the first place, we shall have to try to prove some formula:

$$(y)[F_B(y, g^0) \leftrightarrow y = p^0]$$

in B. Because $F_B(y, x)$ defines a certain function, we may just as well try to prove $F_B(p^0, g^0)$.

(a) Suppose that, for a certain number p, the formula $F_B(p^0, g^0)$ is provable in B. Then we will have $f_B(g) = p + 1$.

This relationship is expressed by the formula $F_B(Sp^0, g^0)$. This formula, essentially, states the provability of $F_B(p^0, g^0)$ in B. Thus, by one of the remarks under (15), if $F_B(p^0, g^0)$ is provable in B, then $F_B(Sp^0, g^0)$ is also provable in B.

However, the two formulas $F_B(p^0, g^0)$ and $F_B(Sp^0, g^0)$ are clearly inconsistent. So if they are both provable in B, then the system B is inconsistent.

(b) The argument under (a) clearly leads to the conclusion that:

If the system B is consistent, then no formula $F_B(p^0, g^0)$ can be provable in B.

Since B has been assumed to be consistent, it follows that in computing $f_B(g)$ we have to apply clause (ij) in the above definition. It follows that we shall have $f_B(g) = 0$.

(c) The argument under (b) leads to the conclusion that:

If the system B is consistent, then $f_B(g) = 0$.

Now the whole discussion above turned around the deducibility of certain formulas. Therefore, it can be entirely restated in the notation of the system B. It follows that in the system B we can prove the formula:

$$NC_B \rightarrow F_B(0, g^0) .$$

(d) Next, suppose that in the system B we could prove the formula NC_B. Then it would be possible to prove in B the formula $F_B(0, g^0)$ and hence, by our conclusion under (b), the system B would be inconsistent. It follows that:

If the system B is consistent, then the formula NC_B cannot be provable in B.

(e) Suppose that in the system B we could prove the formula $\overline{NC_B}$. In an inconsistent system every formula can be proved. Therefore, the formula $\overline{NC_B}$ entails any formula which expresses the provability of some formula. Thus the formula $F_B(SS0, g^0)$, for instance, would be provable in B and so, by our conclusion under (b), the system B would be inconsistent. Consequently:

If the system B *is consistent, then the formula* $\overline{NC_B}$ *cannot be provable in* B.

Since neither NC_B nor $\overline{NC_B}$ can be provable in B, it follows that:
If the system B *is consistent, then it cannot be complete.*

(f) Suppose we had a decision procedure for provability in B. Then, by the argument under (16), (ij), the number-theoretic predicate expressed by Thm_B would be numeralwise representable in A and hence in B. This would enable us to prove in B, for instance, that the formula NC_B is not a theorem of B. Starting from this result, we could clearly prove in B the formula NC_B. Since this is inconsistent with our conclusion under (d), it follows that:
If the system B *is consistent, then there can be no decision procedure for provability in* B.

(19) As a result of the discussion under (18), we can now state the following theorems:

Theorem 35. Neither the deductive system A nor any of its extensions B, insofar as they satisfy the assumptions (I)–(III), can be complete.

Theorem 36. Neither the deductive system A nor any of its extensions B admit of a decision procedure.

Theorem 37. For neither the deductive system A nor for any of its extensions B can the corresponding formula NC be deduced in the system.

They express the celebrated results achieved by K. Gödel (1931) and improved in various respects by J. Barkley Rosser (1936), S. C. Kleene (1936), and others.

(20) It may be added that the procedure described under (16) and under (17) has been found to work for *every* effective method of decision or computation which so far has been taken into consideration, whereas all efforts to establish effective methods for which it would not work have been in vain. Our present knowledge in this domain is based on investigations by K. Gödel (1931), A. Church (1936), S. C. Kleene (1936), E. L. Post (1936), and A. M. Turing (1936) for which the ground had been prepared by earlier work of Th. Skolem, W. Ackermann, and J. Herbrand.

The functions numeralwise representable in the system A (and in many other systems) are those denoted by Kleene, following Herbrand and Gödel, as *general recursive*. According to Church's thesis they are exactly those functions which are effectively computable.

(21) As a corollary to Theorem 36 we have:

Theorem 38. (A. Church, 1937). There is no decision procedure for elementary logic.

Proof. Let Z be any formula in the notation of the deductive system A and let U be the conjunction of the axioms (XVII)–(XIX), of the (finitely many) relevant cases of axiom-schemata (XX) and (XXI), and of the axioms (A1–9). Then, by Theorem 18, the formula Z will be deducible in A if and only if the formula $U \rightarrow Z$ is a thesis of elementary logic.

Thus, if we had a decision procedure for elementary logic, we should also have a decision procedure for the deductive system A. But, by Theorem 36, there can be no decision procedure for the system A; it follows that there cannot be a decision procedure for elementary logic either.

19. SEMANTIC INCOMPLETENESS

The remarkable results in Section 18, *sub* (18), are connected with the fact that there are functions which are not general recursive. Such functions are not numeralwise representable in the system A or in any of its extensions, and there can be no effective method for computing their values. [Several relevant notions will be further explained in Section 22, *sub* (1); *cf.* Section 21, *sub* (6).]

(1) Let us consider once again the function f_B which we defined in Section 18, *sub* (18). We now suppose that the function f_B is numeralwise represented in B by a certain expression $Q(y, x)$. As explained in Section 18, *sub* (17), this means that according as $f_B(m) = n$ or not the formula $Q(n^0, m^0)$ or the formula $\overline{Q(n^0, m^0)}$ is deducible in B.

Let q be the Gödel number of the formula $(x)(y)Q(y, x)$. We wish to compute $f_B(q)$. As before, we consider successively the clauses (i) and (ij) in the definition.

ad (i) Suppose we have $f_\mathrm{B}(q) = p + 1$. Since q happens to be the Gödel number of $(x)(y)Q(y, x)$, this will be the case if:

$$(y)[Q(y, q^0) \leftrightarrow y = p^0] \tag{a}$$

is provable in B. On the other hand, since f_B is numeralwise represented by the expression $Q(y, x)$, we have $f_\mathrm{B}(q) = p + 1$ only if:

$$Q(Sp^0, q^0) \tag{b}$$

is provable in B. But from (a) we infer that:

$$Q(Sp^0, q^0) \leftrightarrow Sp^0 = p^0 \tag{c}$$

and from (b) and (c), that:

$$Sp^0 = p^0 \, .$$

Since B is supposed to be consistent, we clearly cannot have $f_\mathrm{B}(q) = p + 1$. So we turn to clause (ij).

ad (ij) Suppose we have $f_\mathrm{B}(q) = 0$. Since $f_\mathrm{B}(q)$ is numeralwise represented by $Q(y, x)$, it follows that $Q(0, q^0)$ and hence:

$$(y)[Q(y, q^0) \leftrightarrow y = 0]$$

is provable in B. Therefore, we are referred back to clause (i) which we found previously not to work.

Therefore, the function f_B is numeralwise representable neither in the system B nor in the system A.

(2) I wish to stress once more that we must carefully distinguish the *truth* of a formula from its *formal deducibility* (in the deductive system A or in one of its extensions B). The notion of formal deducibility was rigorously defined on the basis of the conceptual apparatus developed in Chapters I–III and usually denoted as *syntax*. The notion of truth, on the other hand, was based on a certain hermeneutics [*cf.* Section 17, *sub* (5)] and thus it involved our pre-scientific knowledge of arithmetic. The incompleteness results discussed in Section 18 can be taken to have a

purely syntactical character, as they are exclusively concerned with the formal deducibility of certain formulas. These results tend to reveal a certain inadequacy in the internal syntactical structure both of the system A and of its extensions B.

The results in the present Section rather point to a certain inadequacy of the syntactical structure of the systems A and B *with respect to our hermeneutics.* Specifically, we have seen that a certain function f_B, though definable by an expression $F_B(y, x)$ in the notation of a given extension B of A, was numeralwise representable neither in B (or A) nor in any extension B' of B. Also NC_A, though true [*cf. Appendix, Section* 41, Theorem 37ᵃ], is not provable in A.

One might be tempted to lay the blame for this inadequacy on the fact that the notion of *definability* [*cf.* Section 18, *sub* (17)] was based on the notion of *truth* and thus involved our hermeneutics; for this reason, the notion of definability might in some respect be unsound.

(3) However, Tarski (1929) has made the observation that in principle it is possible to replace our 'intuitive' *hermeneutics* by a *semantics* developed as rigorously as syntax. In fact, some fragments of such a semantics are already contained in Chapters I and II; for instance, we stated certain rules which determine the truth-values of compound formulas in terms of the truth-values of their components. Similar rules can be stated for formulas in the theory of quantification [*cf. Appendix,* Section 39].

(4) Now suppose that we have developed these fragments into a conceptual apparatus that enables us to give a precise statement of the conditions for a formula U, in the notation of a certain extension B of A, to be true. We can then extend the function w which in Section 17, *sub* (5), was defined for evaluations $t = k^0$, to arbitrary sentences U of B in a manner such that $w(U) = 2$ or $w(U) = 0$, according as U is true or false.

Let us assume in addition that, either by the method explained in Section 18, *sub* (6)–(8), or in some other way, we have restated these truth conditions in the notation of the system B. Then it will be possible to define by means of the notation of the system B a certain function t which satisfies an *adequacy criterion* that *for the moment* may be stated as follows:

(C) $t(g^0) = SS0$ is true if g is the Gödel number of a true formula U_g of B; otherwise, $t(g^0) = 0$ is true [thus, whenever g is the Gödel number of a formula U_g of B, $t(g^0)$ agrees with $w(U_g)$, and otherwise we have $t(g^0) = 0$].

(5) The condition (C) is not a satisfactory one because it still refers to our 'intuitive' hermeneutics. Therefore, it is replaced by Tarski's adequacy criterion which, in the present context, can be stated as follows.
(T) The formulas:

(1)
$$(x)[t(x) = SS0 \to Form_B(x)] ,$$

(2)
$$(x)[t(x) = SS0 \lor t(x) = 0] ,$$

and, whenever g is the Gödel number of a formula U_g of B, the formula:

(3)
$$t(g^0) = SS0 \leftrightarrow U_g ,$$

must be provable in B.

Remark. It was observed under (2) that the *truth* of a formula should be distinguished from its *formal deducibility* (or *provability*). Therefore, it may be asked inhowfar Tarski's criterion (T) hits the mark, because fundamentally we should wish the formulas (1)–(3) to be true, not merely provable in B. In reply to this question it may be observed, first, that we have substituted (T) for (C) in order to avoid reliance on 'intuitive' hermeneutics; for this reason the notion of truth had to be replaced by a different notion. Secondly, the criterion (T) is fully satisfactory with respect to those systems B for which we have the conviction that all provable formulas are true; and even in other systems B (which in the present context are less interesting), the criterion (T) is still a good approximation because in every extension B of A an evaluation in the wider sense, if provable, must be true.

(6) We define a certain number-theoretic predicate E_B, as follows: *The predicate E_B belongs to m if m is the Gödel number of a formula $(v) U(v)$ of B such that $U(m^0)$ is false.*
If $W(m^0, n^0)$ is the formula of A (and hence of B) which expresses the

93

relationship between the respective Gödel numbers m and n of two formulas $(v)\,U(v)$ and $U(m^0)$, then clearly the expression:

$$(y)\,[W(x, y) \to t(y) = 0]$$

defines the predicate E_B. We also note that the formulas $W(m^0, n^0)$ are evaluations in the wider sense.
Now let us take as our formula $(v)\,U(v)$ the formula:

$$(x)(y)\,[W(x, y) \to t(y) = 0]\;;$$

if e is its Gödel number, then the formula corresponding to $U(m^0)$ will be:

(4) $$(y)\,[W(e^0, y) \to t(y) = 0]\;;$$

let f be its Gödel number. Since e and f are in the above relationship, the formula:

(5) $$W(e^0, f^0)\,,$$

being an evaluation in the wider sense, is provable in B. It is easy to see that the formula:

(6) $$(y)\,[W(e^0, y) \to y = f^0]$$

is also provable in B.
On account of criterion (T), and becauce U_f is the formula (4), the formula:

(3) $$t(f^0) = SS0 \leftrightarrow (y)\,[W(e^0, y) \to t(y) = 0]$$

must be provable in B. By Theorem 33, the formula:

(7) $$\overline{0 = SS0}$$

is provable in A and hence in B. Now consider the semantic tableau:

True   False

(2) $(x)[t(x) = SS0 \lor t(x) = 0]$

(3) $t(f^0) = SS0 \leftrightarrow (y)[\ldots]$

(5) $W(e^0, f^0)$

(6) $(y)[W(e^0, y) \rightarrow y = f^0]$

(7) $\overline{0 = SS0}$ $0 = SS0$

$t(f^0) = SS0$ $W(e^0, p)$ $t(f^0) = SS0$

$(y)[\ldots]$ $W(e^0, p) \rightarrow p = f^0$ $(y)[\ldots]$

$W(e^0, f^0) \rightarrow t(f^0) = 0$ (*) $p = f^0$ $W(e^0, p) \rightarrow t(p) = 0$

$t(f^0) = 0$ $t(f^0) = SS0 \lor t(f^0) = 0$ $W(e^0, f^0)$ (*) $t(p) = 0$

$0 = SS0$ $t(f^0) = SS0$ | $t(f^0) = 0$ $W(e^0, p)$

                       (*) $t(f^0) = 0$

The last formula marked (*) follows from the two other ones by the extensionality axiom.

95

This tableau is closed. Because all formulas (2), (3), (5)–(7) were deducible in the system B, it follows that this system is inconsistent.

Theorem 39 (Tarski, 1930). A consistent extension B of the deductive system A cannot make allowance for the definition of a function t which satisfies Tarski's adequacy criterion (T).

Proof. By the argument under (6) any system B which makes allowance for the definition of a function t as described is inconsistent.

The essential clause (3) in Tarski's criterion, currently illustrated by the example:
The sentence 'snow is white' is true if, and only if, snow is white,
may obviously be construed as a modernized version of the traditional definition of truth as *adaequatio rei et intellectus.*

(7) The general conception of semantics underlying the above discussion was developed by Tarski about 1930. The argument under (6) is, of course, closely related to the so-called *Liar Paradox* of Eubulides of Milete, the Liar's statement *'I am lying'* being represented by the formula (4).
In point of fact, Tarski's ideas provide at the same time an analysis of the paradox which, in spite of endless polemics, seems to be final. Pre-scientific logic and arithmetic, as expressed by means of everyday language, constitute so to speak a deductive system B which makes allowance for the definition of a function t. For this reason it cannot be consistent, and its inconsistency manifests itself, among other things, in the emergence of the Liar Paradox.
The inconsistency of this particular system B is due to the fact that everyday language, as a universal medium for expression and communication, is *semantically closed*, that is, makes allowance for the description of its own semantics; the system A and its consistent extensions B, on the other hand, are *semantically non-closed*.

20. LOGIC OF HIGHER ORDER

Although, as we have seen [*cf. Appendix*, Section 41], the system A provides a basis for numerical computation in the widest possible sense, it is by no means satisfactory from the point of view of theoretical arithmetic.

This is illustrated, for instance, by the consistency proof at the end of Section 41. By Theorem 37, this proof cannot be restated within the system A. The reason is that axioms (A1–9) make no provision for the rather obvious recursion on which this proof is based. In fact, practically no proof by recursion is possible within the system A. We shall now discuss the question as to how we can extend the system A so as to fill this gap.

(1) A typical case of the application of proof by recursion is characterized by the following schema:

(A)	0 has the property P,
(B)	If n has the property P, then $n + 1$ has the property P,
(C)	Every natural number n has the property P.

If, in an extension B of A, the property P is defined by an expression $U(x)$, then proof by recursion can be considered as an application of the inference schema:

(A)	$U(0)$,
(B)	$(z)\{U(z) \to U(Sz)\}$,
(C)	$(x)U(x)$;

this inference schema, however, can be reduced to the axiom-schema:

(A9*) $U(0) \to [(z)\{U(z) \to U(Sz)\} \to (x)U(x)]$,

which together with the premisses (A) and (B) yields the conclusion (C), because the systems B make allowance for the application of *modus ponens*.

(2) Let A* be the deductive system based upon the axioms (A1–8) and on axiom-schema (A9*). It may be objected that so far we have only made allowance for deductive systems based on finitely many axioms. It is, however, not difficult to extend our previous results so as to cover the case of the system A* as well. Moreover, under (4) we shall see that A* can be replaced by a system based on finitely many axioms.

Axiom (A9) is easily obtained as a theorem of A* if in axiom-schema (A9*) we take as expression $U(x)$ the expression: $x = 0 \lor (Ey)\{x = Sy\}$. Conversely, this case of axiom-schema (A9*) follows immediately from axiom (A9). Not every case of (A9*) can, however, be obtained in this manner, and it is even known (C. Ryll-Nardzewski, 1952) that this axiom-schema cannot be replaced by any finite number of its applications.

(3) One might still contemplate the following extension of axiom-schema (A9*). Suppose $U(x, v)$ contains a variable v different from x and from z. Then we might accept as an axiom:

(A9**) $(v)\{U(0, v) \rightarrow [(z)\{U(z, v) \rightarrow U(Sz, v)\} \rightarrow (x)U(x, v)]\}$.

This formula, however, can be deduced from suitable applications of axiom-schema (A9*).

(4) We introduce new variables X, Y, Z, ..., V, V', V'', ... which are meant to range over the family of all classes of natural numbers. These variables will appear in atomic expressions:

$$t \in X, \ t \in Y, \ t \in Z, \ ..., \ t \in V, \ t \in V', \ t \in V'', \ ...,$$

where t is an arbitrary term; $t \in V$ is meant to express the condition for an individual $w(t)$ to belong to a class $w(V)$. We introduce corresponding quantifiers (X), (Y), (Z), ..., (EX), (EY), (EZ), ...; stipulation (F2) in Section 8 must be suitably expanded. Finally, our methods of deduction must be adapted in a rather obvious manner.

We can now replace axiom-schema (A9*) by a single axiom, namely:

(A9⁰) $(V)\{0 \in V \rightarrow [(z)\{z \in V \rightarrow Sz \in V\} \rightarrow (x)(x \in V)]\}$.

However, if nothing more is done, this axiom will be a poor substitute, even for our original axiom (A9). If we wish to apply axiom (A9⁰), then suitable values for the variable V must be available; in other words, besides (A9⁰) we must introduce axioms which guarantee the existence of certain classes.

A first approach is, to adopt the axiom-schema:

(XXII⁰) $(EX)(x)[x \in X \leftrightarrow U(x)]$,

98

where $U(x)$ may be an arbitrary expression in the notation of the system A. In this manner we shall obtain a deductive system which, as far as theorems in the original notation of the system A are concerned, coincides with the system A*. For an application of reduction schema (vij[b]) to (XXII[0]) produces a formula: $(x)[x \in P \leftrightarrow U(x)]$. Then an application of reduction schema (vi[a]) to (A9[0]) produces a formula which together with $(x)[x \in P \leftrightarrow U(x)]$ is exactly equivalent to the corresponding application of axiom-schema (A9*).

(5) A proper extension as compared to the system A* is achieved if we adopt the axiom-schema:

(XXII) $(EX)(x)[x \in X \leftrightarrow U(x)]$,

where now the expression $U(x)$ may contain bound class variables.
Again, one might contemplate strengthening the system A^0 thus obtained by introducing variables $R, R', R'', \ldots$ ranging over the family of all relations between natural numbers. From this step, however, no proper strengthening would result since with each relation R between natural numbers we may associate a class V of natural numbers, as follows:

$$z \in V \leftrightarrow (Ex)(Ey)[z = 2^x \cdot 3^y \ \& \ xRy],$$

$$xRy \leftrightarrow (z)[z = 2^x \cdot 3^y \rightarrow z \in V].$$

Therefore, an expression $(R)[— R —]$ can always be replaced by a suitable expression:

$$(V)[(z)\{z \in V \rightarrow (Ex)(Ey)[z = 2^x \cdot 3^y]\} \rightarrow \{— V —\}].$$

Let us observe that if the applications of axiom-schema (XXII) are counted among the logical axioms, then the system A^0 is again based on a finite axiom system containing (A1–8) and (A9[0]).

(6) A further strengthening as compared to the system A^0 can be achieved by introducing variables ranging over the set of all families of classes of natural numbers and adding suitable logical axioms. A detailed study of this system is, however, beyond the scope of this book.

(7) The system A^0, though stronger than A^*, still satisfies assumptions (I)–(III) as stated in Section 18, *sub* (11). It follows that there are true formulas, even *in the original notation of the system* A, which cannot be proved in the system A^0.

Thus the passage to a logic of higher order characterized by the introduction of new types of variables does not essentially change the general situation.

CHAPTER VI

THE THEORY OF DEFINITION

21. INTRODUCTION

It may cause some surprise that the theory of definition is presented in the last Chapter of this book and not, in accordance with a long tradition, in its first Chapter. This apparent anomaly is due to the fact that, according to contemporary conceptions, the theory of definition presupposes the methodology of deductive disciplines which, in turn, is based upon the theory of deduction. Although various methodological concepts have already been explained along with our treatment of formalized logic and arithmetic, a brief survey of the principles of methodology will not be out of place.

(1) A deductive discipline T is characterised by a certain set K of specific *axioms* and by an underlying system of logic. The theorems of T are those sentences Z which can be deduced from K by means of this logical system. The formal methods developed in Chapters I–IV enable us to give a precise description of logical systems and of the methods of deduction which they represent. In accordance with current practice, we shall identify a deductive discipline T with the set of all its theorems.

If the discipline T has been formalized, then the axioms in K will present themselves as formulas, and the predicate parameters (as well as, eventually, the individual constants and function symbols) which appear in these formulas correspond to the so-called *primitive notions* of T. For instance, the axioms (A1–9) in Section 17 contained notations corresponding to the concepts *zero, successor, addition, multiplication,* and *exponentiation* which, therefore, constitute the primitive notions of that specific version of arithmetic of which A constitutes a formalization. The *theorems* of A were obtained from its axioms by deduction in accordance with elementary logic with equality and terms.

Likewise, the *defined notions* of A are obtained from its primitive notions by means of definitions. For a given logical system, definitions must satisfy certain *formal rules of definition*.

(2) Let us first consider an example, namely, the definition of $<$ which in Section 18, *sub* (4) could not be given sufficient attention. Its introduction requires that we first expand stipulation (F1) [*cf. Appendix*, Section 37, *sub* (1)] so as to make allowance for the introduction of new atoms:

$$t < t'.$$

Only then is it possible to state the definition:

(A$<$) $$(x)(y)[x < y \leftrightarrow (Ez)\{x + Sz = y\}].$$

(3) We can now state for elementary logic the following *formal rule of definition*. Let F be a 'fresh' k-ary predicate parameter, that is, a k-ary predicate parameter not appearing in the axioms in K and not previously introduced by definition. We first expand stipulation (F1) so as to make allowance for the introduction of new atoms:

$$F(t_1, t_2, \ldots, t_k).$$

Then let $U(v_1, v_2, \ldots, v_k)$ be any expression (*cf.* Section 8) containing only predicate parameters (and, eventually, individual constants and function symbols) previously introduced. Then the formula:

$$(v_1)(v_2) \ldots (v_k)[F(v_1, v_2, \ldots, v_k) \leftrightarrow U(v_1, v_2, \ldots, v_k)]$$

will be admissible as a definition of F. This formula will henceforth be treated on the same footing as the axioms in K and as the definitions previously introduced.

(4) Suppose that the axioms in K contain the predicate parameters A and B and let the structure $\mathbf{M} = \langle \mathbf{S}, \mathbf{A}, \mathbf{B} \rangle$ be a model for all formulas in K. We wish to show that $\mathbf{M}$ can be transformed in exactly one manner into a structure $\mathbf{M}' = \langle \mathbf{S}, \mathbf{A}, \mathbf{B}, \mathbf{F} \rangle$ which is a model for all formulas in K and, in addition, for the above definition of F.

(i) Let F be chosen as follows: the predicate $\mathbf{F}$ will hold for the elements $m_1, m_2, \ldots, m_k$ of $\mathbf{S}$ if and only if the formula:

$$U(m_1{}^*, m_2{}^*, \ldots, m_k{}^*)$$

is true for **M**. Then clearly all formulas:

$$F(m_1{}^*, m_2{}^*, \ldots, m_k{}^*) \leftrightarrow U(m_1{}^*, m_2{}^*, \ldots, m_k{}^*)$$

will be true for $\mathbf{M'} = \; < \mathbf{S, A, B, F} >$ and hence the above definition of F will also be true for **M'**.

(ij) Let **F'** be different from **F** as characterized under (i); then clearly some formula:

$$F(m_1{}^*, m_2{}^*, \ldots, m_k{}^*) \leftrightarrow U(m_1{}^*, m_2{}^*, \ldots, m_k{}^*)$$

must be false for the structure $< \mathbf{S, A, B, F'} >$. It follows that the formula:

$$(v_1)(v_2) \ldots (v_k) [F(v_1, v_2, \ldots, v_k) \leftrightarrow U(v_1, v_2, \ldots, v_k)]$$

is also false for this structure which therefore cannot be a model for this definition of F. Thus we have:

Theorem 40. Theorems 26–32 and 8ᵃ for elementary logic and its various extensions still hold true if we make allowance for the introduction of defined notions under the above formal rule of definition.

(5) Strictly speaking, Theorem 40 still presupposes:

Theorem 41. From the introduction of a defined notion under the above formal rule of definition no contradiction can arise.

Proof. Suppose that the axiom set K is consistent and that F has been introduced by a definition of the above kind. Then, by Theorem 29 there exists a model **M** for the set K and, as shown under (i), this model can be transformed into a model **M'** for K and for the definition of F. Thus, by Theorem 29 the set K' which results from adding this definition to K must also be consistent.

Remark. The above proof of Theorem 41, simple though it may seem, is not acceptable from the point of view of Hilbert's finitistic formalism because it is based on Theorem 29 which involved both infinitistic methods of proof and our 'intuitive' hermeneutics. Therefore, it will be instructive also to present a finitistic proof, based on an idea that goes back to Pascal.

Proof. Let W be the above definition by which F has been introduced and suppose that from (K, W) some contradiction, say $U \,\&\, \bar{U}$, can be deduced. Suppose that the deduction is actually given in the form of a

103

closed semantic tableau. In this deduction we replace each occurrence of an expression $F(t_1, t_2, \ldots, t_k)$ by an occurrence of its *definiens* $U(t_1, t_2, \ldots, t_k)$. Then:

(i) each formula is replaced by a formula as characterized by the stipulations (F1–3);

(ij) the given closed semantic tableau is transformed into a semantic tableau constructed and closed under the relevant schemata;

(iij) the axioms in K and the conclusion U & $\bar{U}$ are not affected;

(iv) the formula W is replaced by the formula:

$$(v_1)(v_2) \ldots (v_k)[U(v_1, v_2, \ldots, v_k) \leftrightarrow U(v_1, v_2, \ldots, v_k)]$$

which clearly is a thesis of elementary logic.

It follows that the conclusion U & $\bar{U}$ can already be deduced from the set K alone, and thus the contradiction has not arisen from the introduction of the defined notion F. Conversely, if the set K is consistent, then the set (K, W) will be consistent as well.

(6) In introducing a defined notion F it is usually not our main concern that we have to comply with the above formal rule of definition. The normal situation can rather be described as follows. We have a set K of axioms in which certain predicate parameters A and B appear, and a certain model $\mathbf{M} = \,< \mathbf{S}, \mathbf{A}, \mathbf{B} >$ for K. Moreover we have in mind a certain predicate $\mathbf{F}$ which refers to the elements of $\mathbf{S}$.

We now wish to define F in such a manner that the structure $\mathbf{M}' = \,= \,< \mathbf{S}, \mathbf{A}, \mathbf{B}, \mathbf{F} >$ becomes a model of the set (K, W). Thus the *definiendum* $\mathbf{F}$ is given and we have to look for a suitable *definiens* $U(\ldots)$. If such a *definiens* can be found, $\mathbf{F}$ is said to be *definable* in K. We have met with such a situation in Section 19, *sub* (6).

22. DEFINABILITY OF PRIMITIVE NOTIONS

In Section 21 we were concerned with definitions by which *new* notions $F, \ldots$ were introduced into a deductive discipline T, previously characterized by a set K of axioms containing certain primitive notions $A, B, \ldots$. The conception of one of these primitive notions being defined would not fit into the framework of that discussion.

(1) A few more remarks on methodology in general may prepare the ground for an explanation of this conception. We usually require the axioms U_1, U_2, ..., U_m in a set K to be: (i) *consistent*, (ij) *independent*, and (iij) *complete*.

ad (i) A set K is said to be *consistent* if it does not permit the deduction of two contradictory formulas X and $\bar{X}$. It is not difficult to show that an inconsistent set K permits the deduction of any formula Z. Thus if a given set K does not permit the deduction of a certain formula Z, it follows that K is consistent; *cf.* Theorem 35ᵃ.

ad (ij) The axiom U_p is said to be *independent* of the remaining axioms U_1, U_2, ..., U_{p-1}, U_{p+1}, ..., U_m in K if it is not deducible from these axioms. If U_p is *not* independent, then the set of all theorems of T is not affected by the omission of U_p from K. For in developing T we may first deduce U_p from the set K' of all remaining axioms, and then we may, as before, deduce all other theorems from the set $(K', U_p) = K$; *cf.* Theorems 19 and 20.

ad (iij) The notion of *completeness* can be understood in various different manners, two of which will be discussed.

(I) In a purely *formal* or *syntactical* sense the set K can be said to be complete if, whenever X is a formula in the notation of T, either that formula X itself or its negation $\bar{X}$ can be deduced from K.

(II) Suppose, on the other hand, that the discipline T is meant to study a certain class C of structures $\mathbf{M} = < \mathbf{S}, \mathbf{A}, \mathbf{B}, \ldots >$. Then K will be said to be complete in a *semantical* sense if, whenever a formula X in the notation of T is true for all structures $\mathbf{M}$ in C, it is deducible from K. If C consists of just one structure $\mathbf{M}$, then a semantically complete set K will also be formally complete as defined under (I). In Chapter V we studied certain sets A and B which were meant to study just one structure $\mathbf{M}$, namely, the set of all natural numbers with its familiar operations. We found that none of these sets could be formally or semantically complete.

(2) Now let $A, B, \ldots, F$ be the primitive notions of a deductive discipline T. In order to study the effect of omitting the primitive notion F, we consider the set T^0 of all theorems of T in which the notion F does not appear; let K^0 be a set of axioms from which all theorems in T^0 can be deduced and which also does not contain the notion F.

(3) In accordance with the formal rule of definition in Section 21 *sub* (3), the notion F can now be re-introduced by adding to K^0 a definition W of F in terms of A, B, ... Let T' be the set of all theorems deducible from the set (K^0, W). We consider the various relationships which may exist between the sets T and T'. Obviously the following situations can be anticipated:

  (i) for a suitable choice of W, we have $T' \subseteq T$;

  (ij) it is not possible to choose W in such a manner that we shall have $T' \subseteq T$; however, for a suitable choice of W the systems T and T' can be merged into a consistent system T'';

(iij) for every choice of W the merger of T and T' produces an inconsistent system T''.

ad (i) From $W \in T'$ and $T' \subseteq T$, it follows that $W \in T$. Thus the definition W is a theorem of T. In this case, we say that the primitive notion F is *provably definable* in terms of A, B, . . . and with respect to T. Now let X be any formula in the notation of T and let X^0 be obtained from X by replacing each occurrence of an expression $F(\ldots)$ by an occurrence of its definiens $U(\ldots)$ as given by the definition W. In this manner the axiom set K for T will be transformed into a set K^0 in which the notion F no longer appears. As (by the argument used in the second proof of Theorem 41) a formula X deducible from K is replaced by a formula X^0 deducible from K^0 and since all formulas in K^0 are deducible from K whereas all formulas in T^0 remain unchanged, it follows that K^0 provides a suitable axiom set for T^0. Conversely, if X^0 is in T^0 and hence deducible from K^0, then clearly X is deducible from (K^0, W). It follows that $T \subseteq T'$. So we have:

Theorem 42. A primitive notion F is provably definable in terms of A, B, . . . and with respect to T if and only if a suitable definition W is deducible from the axiom set K of T; and if the set K^0 is obtained by replacing in the axioms U in K each occurrence of an expression $F(\ldots)$ by an occurrence of its *definiens* as given by W, then all theorems of T are deducible from (K^0, W) and every formula deducible from (K^0, W) is a theorem of T.

ad (ij) Suppose that a suitable formula W is a theorem of T. Then we can in the above manner construct an axiom set K^0 for T^0 and since all formulas in (K^0, W) are theorems of T, it follows that $K' \subseteq K$, which contradicts our supposition. However, because all axioms U in K as well as W are theorems in a consistent extension T'' of T, it follows that the set (K, W) is consistent if W is suitably chosen. We say in this case that the primitive notion F is *compatibly definable* in terms of A, B, ... and with respect to T.

Theorem 43. A primitive notion F is compatibly definable in terms of A, B, ... and with respect to T if and only if it is provably deducible in terms of these notions and with respect to a suitable consistent extension T'' of T.

ad (iij) Suppose that F is compatibly definable in terms of A, B, ... and with respect to T. Then F is provably definable in terms of these notions and with respect to a suitable consistent extension T'' of T. Let W be the corresponding definition of F in terms of A, B, ... Now all axioms of T^0 are contained in T and hence in T'', and so is the definition W. Since all axioms in the axiom set (K^0, W) for T' are contained in T'', it follows that $T' \subseteq T''$; since T'' is an extension of T, we have $T \subseteq T''$. Therefore, the system which results from the merger of T and T' is included in T''; it follows that this system must be consistent. But this contradicts our supposition. It follows that F cannot be compatibly definable in terms of A, B, ... and with respect to T. Therefore, we say that in this case the primitive notion F is *essentially undefinable* in terms of A, B, ... and with respect to T.

(4) The *independence* of a primitive notion as currently understood is the negation of its *provable definability*. *Compatible definability* is a more general concept than provable definability and thus its negation, *essential undefinability*, must be regarded as a strengthened form of independence. K. L. de Bouvère (1959) who introduced these last two concepts and cleared up their connections with independence and (provable) definability as currently understood has observed, moreover, that various well-known cases of independence of primitive notions are really cases of essential undefinability with respect to relatively weak systems T.

23. PADOA'S METHOD

It follows from our above treatment of the principles of logic that such

107

notions as consistency and independence, even though they can be adequately defined within the framework of a theory of formal deduction, are nevertheless closely connected with semantics. In the practice of current mathematical research these connections manifest themselves by the fact that often we establish the consistency of an axiom set K by exhibiting a structure $\mathbf{M}$ for which all formulas in K are true, and the independence of an axiom U_p with respect to the axioms U_1, U_2, ..., U_{p-1}, U_{p+1}, ..., U_m by exhibiting a structure $\mathbf{M}$ for which these last-mentioned formulas are true whereas the formula U_p is false (*cf.* Theorems 29 and 30).

(1) It is only natural to ask whether there exists a similar method for showing that a certain primitive notion F is independent with respect to the other primitive notions A, B, ... of a deductive discipline T. There is indeed such a method which was first described and applied by A. Padoa (1899).

In order to understand the method more easily, let us return to the case of a provably definable notion F. In that case, the system T could be obtained from T^0, the part of T which does not involve the notion F, by simply adding a suitable definition W of F in terms of A, B, ... Let $\mathbf{M} = \langle\, S, A, B, ..., F\, \rangle$ be any model of T. Then clearly $\mathbf{M}^0 = \langle\, S, A, B, ... \,\rangle$ will be a model of T^0. And, conversely, each model $\mathbf{M}^0$ of T^0 can be transformed in exactly one manner into a model $\mathbf{M}$ of T; this was shown in Section 21, *sub* (4).

(2) Now suppose that we can find two models $\mathbf{M}' = \langle\, S', A', B', ... F'\, \rangle$ and $\mathbf{M}'' = \langle\, S'', A'', B'', ..., F''\, \rangle$ of T such that S' is the same set as S'', A' the same predicate as A'', B' the same predicate as B'', ..., whereas F' is different from F''. Then F is independent of A, B, ... with respect to T.

For suppose F to be provably definable. The two models $\mathbf{M}'$ and $\mathbf{M}''$ clearly produce the same model $\mathbf{M}^0 = \langle\, S', A', B', ... \,\rangle = \langle\, S'', A'', B'', ... \,\rangle$ of T^0. And, by the observation under (1), this model can be transformed in exactly one manner into a model $\mathbf{M}$ of T. But this conclusion clearly contradicts the fact that there are two models $\mathbf{M}'$ and $\mathbf{M}''$ as described. It follows that F cannot be provably definable and so F is independent. This discussion shows that the application of Padoa's method is justified.

(3) It follows from Gödel's completeness theorem (*cf.* Theorems 29 and 30) that whenever an axiom set K is consistent and whenever an axiom U_p is independent there is a structure **M** by which this fact can be demonstrated.

A similar result was established by the present author (1953) in connection with the independence of primitive notions. Thus we have:

Theorem 44. A primitive notion F is independent with respect to the other primitive notions A, B, ... of a deductive discipline T if and only if there are two models **M'** and **M"** of T by which this fact can be demonstrated in accordance with Padoa's method.

(4) Apparently this result does not follow directly from Gödel's completeness theorem for elementary logic. In order to prepare the ground for the explanation of its proof (see *Appendix*, Section 42), it will be helpful to have still another look at the theoretical basis of Padoa's method.

The two above structures **M'** and **M"** can be merged into a single structure **M*** = < **S*, A*, B***, ..., **F', F"** >, where **S*** coincides with **S'** and **S"**, **A*** with **A'** and **A"**, **B*** with **B'** and **B"**, ..., and where **F'** and **F"** are the same as before. The structure **M*** is characterized by the fact that it is a model for the set $(K', K'', \bar{Z})$, where K' and K'' are obtained from K by substituting, respectively, F' and F'' for F and where Z is the formula:

$$(v_1)(v_2) \ldots (v_k)[F'(v_1, v_2, \ldots, v_k) \leftrightarrow F''(v_1, v_2, \ldots, v_k)].$$

If it is not possible to find suitable models **M'** and **M"**, it follows that there can be no model **M*** and hence the set $(K', K'', \bar{Z})$ must be inconsistent; thus the formula Z must be deducible from the set (K', K'').

(5) In the case of elementary logic, the main difficulty consists in showing that any given deduction of Z from $(K' \ K'')$ can be converted into a deduction of a suitable formula W from K.

In the case of higher-order logic, this step is relatively simple, as was shown by Tarski in 1935. If Z can be deduced from K, then we can take as W the formula:

$$(v_1)(v_2) \ldots (v_k)[F(v_1, v_2, \ldots, v_k) \leftrightarrow (X)\{K^0 \rightarrow X(v_1, v_2, \ldots, v_k)\}],$$

where K^0 is the conjunction of the formulas obtained from the axioms in K by replacing each occurrence of the predicate parameter F by an occurrence of a 'fresh' predicate variable X.

However, in the case of higher-order logic we must be prepared for other complications which I shall not discuss.

(6) On the other hand, it seems worth while briefly to mention the following variant to Padoa's method. Suppose that we find a model $\mathbf{M}^0$ of T^0 which cannot, by any choice of a predicate $\mathbf{F}$, be converted into a model $\mathbf{M}$ of T. Then again it clearly follows that the primitive notion F is independent.

A first example of the application of this method was discussed by the present author in 1956. Its methodological background was then very thoroughly examined by K. L. de Bouvère (1959) who pointed out, among other things, that by a model $\mathbf{M}^0$ as described not only the independence of the primitive notion F, but in addition its essential undefinability, is demonstrated.

It seems that in this case no obvious counterpart to Gödel's completeness theorem or to the present author's result concerning Padoa's method is to be expected. However, the results of further research must be awaited.

24. DEFINITION-THEORETIC INCOMPLETENESS

The construction of a deductive discipline T is usually motivated by semantical considerations as indicated in Section 21, *sub* (6), and in Section 22, *sub* (1), *ad* (iij). So we shall select as primitive notions such concepts as have a clear sense with respect to all structures $\mathbf{M}$ in the class C from which we start and as axioms such statements as are true for all these structures. Then all defined notions will also have a clear sense and likewise all theorems of T will be true for all structures $\mathbf{M}$ in C.

(1) Of course, we should wish to select our primitive notions and axioms once for all in such a manner that we have a complete basis for defining all further relevant concepts and for formulating and proving all further relevant truths.

In our study of the formalization of arithmetic (*cf.* Chapter V), however, we made in this connection a most disappointing discovery. We found that there exist formulas in the notation of the deductive system A which on the basis of our axioms (A1–9) we could neither establish nor refute. And, what was much more serious, an extension B of A which satisfies a few very plausible assumptions could never fill all the gaps revealed in the system A. For every system B, again, there are formulas which can be neither proven nor disproven in B. This surprising phenomenon is a manifestation of what can be denoted as the *deduction-theoretic incompleteness of formalized arithmetic.*

(2) Similarly we found that for the deductive system A there exist arithmetical concepts which cannot be defined by an expression $U(x)$ in the notation of A. Again an extension B of A can only make up for part of the deficiencies of A; for each system B we can find arithmetical concepts not definable in B. I may still give another example of such a concept.

(G) A natural number m will be said to have the property G_B, if it is the Gödel number of a formula $(v) U(v)$ such that m does not have the property defined by $U(v)$.

Let the property G_B be defined by a formula $G(x)$ of B and let g be the Gödel number of the formula $(x) G(x)$.

(i) Suppose that g has the property G_B. Then it cannot have the property defined by $G(x)$; hence g cannot have the property G_B.

(ij) Since g cannot have the property G_B, it follows that g must have the property defined by $G(x)$; so g must have the property G_B.

This argument shows that the property G_B cannot be defined by an expression $G(x)$ in the notation of B. This and other similar phenomena demonstrate the *definition-theoretic incompleteness of formalized arithmetic.*

(3) The grave character of these two forms of incompleteness in formalized arithmetic will be fully realised if we take into account the fact that many of the most important theories of pure mathematics are extensions of the deductive system A. As examples I mention the (non-elementary) theory of real numbers and (non-elementary) Euclidean geometry. It follows that these theories are also both deduction-theoretically and definition-theoretically incomplete.

CHAPTER VII

ON MACHINES WHICH PROVE THEOREMS

25. INTRODUCTION – COMPUTATION AND FORMAL DEDUCTION

The invention of computation goes far back in the history of the human mind. And, even though for many centuries it remained technically inefficient and theoretically crude, it fascinated mankind already in this underdeveloped stage. Perhaps the very defects in the art of computation offer the best explanation of the fact that, for a long time, it was considered a kind of black magic.

At any rate, the fascination inspired by the art of computation explains why, at a certain moment, a properly scientific interest in numbers developed. At first, this interest naturally focused on the study of numbers as individuals. There still remain clear traces of a stage in the development of arithmetic where the factorization of a large integer or the discovery of a large prime were considered as brilliant achievements. Such investigations, however, could in themselves hardly lead to any important progress in the art of computation. Two further steps were necessary. In the first place, scientific interest had to shift from numbers as individuals to general properties of numbers; this step eventually led to a considerable deepening of theoretic insight. Secondly, a deeper insight into the general properties of numbers made it possible to invent more convenient systems of notation. Finally, the combination of a deeper insight with a better notation gave rise to the development of more and more powerful computational techniques.

It has been observed long ago that there is a striking analogy between computation and formal deduction. On the basis of this analogy, we may expect the development of arithmetic and logic to be quite similar. This expectation is corroborated by the facts, with this understanding, however, that there is an enormous lag in time. In fact, the present stage of development in logic may well be compared to a rather primitive stage in the development of arithmetic. Formal logic is still often looked upon as a kind of esoteric doctrine; and a man who succeeds in deducing a certain theorem from axioms by which apparently it was not entailed, creates a similar stir as was formerly elicited by a calculator factorizing some large integer previously believed to be prime.

26. FORMAL DEDUCTION AND COMPUTING MACHINES

On the other hand, in view of recent developments in the design and the construction of very powerful automatic computers and in the art of programming their operations, it is only natural to consider the possibility of using such computers in solving certain problems in formal deduction. This possibility is also strongly suggested by the fact that actually sentential logic plays a certain role in the design of computers and that Gödel's method of arithmetization enables us, in principle, to convert every logical problem into an arithmetical one.

This matter was first taken up by A. Newell and H. A. Simon (1956) and subsequently discussed by H. L. Gelernter (1957), A. Robinson (1957), H. L. Gelernter and N. Rochester (1958), the present author (1958), P. C. Gilmore (1959), and by D. Prawitz, H. Prawitz, and N. Voghera (1959); these last-mentioned authors actually succeeded in realising a mechanical proof procedure in an electronic computer. The work of Trenchard More (1957), a student of C. E. Shannon, has not appeared in print.

In Sections 27–31, I intend to show that further progress in the domain under discussion strongly depends on the development of a deeper insight into the general properties of formal deductions but that, as in the case of arithmetic, we must anticipate that a deeper insight on the purely theoretical level will not in itself be sufficient. We need in addition a suitable notation. And what we need is not only a convenient notation for the formulas which appear in formal deductions; we need a concise notation for formal deductions as well.

27. THE SUBFORMULA PRINCIPLE

Newell and Simon discuss the construction of a machine which is able to deduce theses of the two-valued (or classical) sentential logic on an axiomatic basis. Such a basis is taken to consist of a certain (finite) number of axioms, combined with two inference schemata, namely:

 (i) the *substitution schema* which allows us to substitute arbitrary formulas $U, V, W, \ldots$ for the atoms $A, B, C, \ldots$ which appear in a given thesis T, and

(ij) the *modus ponens* which allows us, from two given theses S and $S \rightarrow T$, to infer the thesis T.

For instance, if we restrict ourselves to the case of purely implicational logic, then we may start from the axioms:

(I^0)	$A \rightarrow (B \rightarrow A)$,
(II^0)	$[A \rightarrow (B \rightarrow C)] \rightarrow [(A \rightarrow B) \rightarrow (A \rightarrow C)]$,
(III^0)	$[(A \rightarrow B) \rightarrow A] \rightarrow A$.

It is argued by Newell and Simon that the success of an attempt to deduce a certain thesis T on a given axiomatic basis depends upon the selection of the right substituends $U, V, W, \ldots$. These substituends must be selected from the infinite stock of all formulas and, hence, either the machine has to exhaust all possible substitutions (the '*British Museum method*', which is found to be too time-consuming), or it must be equipped with certain '*heuristic*' devices which enable it to select in advance those substitutions which are most likely to prove successful. These heuristic devices are to be copied from the manner in which a human being would use its intelligence in a similar situation.

However interesting and, perhaps, enlightening such an '*anthropomorphic*' approach may be, there is no real need for the introduction of heuristic devices. In fact, suppose we wish to deduce a certain thesis, for instance:

$$[(A \rightarrow B) \rightarrow C] \rightarrow [(A \rightarrow C) \rightarrow C],$$

on a certain given axiomatic basis. Then it is possible to enumerate, in advance, all formulas which ought to be taken into account as substituends; they are:

 (i) the thesis to be deduced;

(ij) the *proper subformulas* of the thesis, namely:

$$(A \rightarrow B) \rightarrow C, (A \rightarrow C) \rightarrow C, A \rightarrow B, A \rightarrow C, A, B, \text{ and } C;$$

(iij) certain simple combinations of the formulas under (i) and (ij), depending upon the axiomatic basis that has been chosen.

114

So the machine can first construct an exhaustive list of all possible substituends, then carry out all possible substitutions in the axioms, and finally go through all possible applications of *modus ponens*; the above thesis must appear among the formulas which result. And, if instead of the above thesis, we consider a certain formula U which happens not to be a thesis, then again the machine will go through all the above operations, but U will not appear among the formulas which result. The above facts will be more fully explained in the next Section.

28. SEMANTIC TABLEAUX AND NATURAL DEDUCTION

The discussion in Section 27 was meant to show the importance of taking into account all relevant theoretic insight which is available at present. I now turn to my second point, namely, the need for a concise notation for formal deductions.

With a view to this requirement I may mention in the first place the method of semantic tableaux. This method was introduced [*cf*. Section 3, *sub* (4)] as a convenient presentation of the familiar *truth-table analysis* which results, for instance, with respect to the formula considered in Section 27, in the conclusion that this formula is a *logical identity*.

However, the tableau may also be considered in a different manner, in which case it is construed [*cf*. Section 3, *sub* (7)] as a *formal deduction*. It is one of the most attractive features of (closed) semantic tableaux, considered as a method of formal deduction, that this method satisfies the *subformula principle* in its strictest form: *all formulas which appear in a deduction of a thesis U are subformulas of U.*

However, closed semantic tableaux do not present the typical shape in which deductions normally appear. So we introduced two further methods of formal deduction, namely:

(i) *axiomatic deduction* [*cf*. Section 4 and Section 5, *sub* (5)] which is closely related to 'Hilbert-type' deduction as considered by Newell and Simon, and,

(ij) *natural deduction* [*cf*. Section 40] in a system which is closely related to Gentzen's system NK.

These systems satisfy the subformula principle only in a slightly weakened form. In the system of natural deduction, the deduction of a thesis U

115

may involve, besides the subformulas of U, the negations of these sub-formulas as well.

For the above system of 'Hilbert-type' deduction, the situation is slightly more involved. In the first place, we use in Peirce's Law (III^0) as substituends all atoms appearing in U; let $U_1, U_2, \ldots, U_k$ be the substitution results; then in axioms (I^0) and (II^0) we use as substituends both the formulas $U, U_1, U_2, \ldots, U_k$ as well as all their subformulas. It should be mentioned, however, that on the basis of more profound theoretic insight, the number of relevant substitutions might be substantially reduced; such a reduction will, for instance, result if, adapting Lyndon's idea [*cf*. Section 42, *sub* (8)], we make a distinction between *positive* and *negative* subformulas.

A further study of semantic tableaux might lead to further metamathematical results which would be of some importance with a view to the problems discussed in this Chapter.

29. COMPLICATIONS

In principle, the method of semantic tableaux can be said to provide a theoretical basis for the construction of a '*logic theory machine*' up to the problem of setting up the program.

There are, however, certain complications which are connected with Church's Theorem [*cf*. Section 18, *sub* (21)] concerning the impossibility of an effective decision procedure for elementary logic, and, therefore, appear in all adequate formalizations of this logical domain. A study of certain semantic tableaux may help us in understanding the mechanism behind these complications.

Consider, for instance, the semantic tableau in Section 14, *sub* (2). This example, although relatively simple in itself, shows that we must be prepared in general to meet with a quite irregular succession of introductions of new individual parameters $a, b, c, \ldots$, of splittings into sub-tableaux, and of closures of some of the subtableaux obtained. Very soon indeed a tableau may become so involved as to make the operation of the machine too time-consuming.

It will be clear that the number $n(U)$ of the individual parameters $a, b, c, \ldots$, which must be introduced in a tentative deduction of a given formula U is the crucial factor here. Once $n(U)$ has been fixed, the construction of a semantic tableau reduces to a finite procedure. Hence, the problem of simplifying this construction (or, at any rate, of avoiding unnecessary complications) breaks up into two partial problems:

(i) minimizing or fixing the value of $n(U)$,

(ij) for given $n(U)$, simplifying the tableau construction.

Now it would, of course, be very nice if we could once for all fix $n(U)$ in such a manner that, whenever a formula U is at all deducible, its deduction can be achieved by introducing at most $n(U)$ individual parameters. However, this would imply the existence of an effective decision procedure, which is excluded by Church's Theorem.

Before going more deeply into point (i), it will be good to devote a few words to point (ij). As an illustration, we consider the tableau for the formula:

$$(x)(y)[A(x) \lor B(y)] \to \{(x)A(x) \lor (y)B(y)\}$$

	True			False	
(2)	$(x)(y)[A(x) \lor B(y)]$		(1)	$(x)(y)[\ldots] \to \{\ldots\}$	
(8)	$(y)[A(a) \lor B(y)]$		(3)	$(x)A(x) \lor (y)B(y)$	
(9)	$A(a) \lor B(a)$		(4)	$(x)A(x)$	
(10)	$A(a) \lor B(b)$		(5)	$(y)B(y)$	
(11)	$(y)[A(b) \lor B(y)]$		(6)	$A(a)$	
(12)	$A(b) \lor B(a)$		(7)	$B(b)$	
(13)	$A(b) \lor B(b)$				

Of the four formulas (9), (10), (12), and (13), it is clearly sufficient to consider formula (10). This leads to one splitting of the tableau, immediately followed by the closure of each of the two resulting subtableaux. However, if we overlook this fact, we are compelled to carry out 4 successive splittings, followed by the closure of each of the 16 subtableaux which result. This example shows how, by an intelligent selection of the relative order in which the operations are carried out, we are able to simplify the construction. It remains to be seen to what extent it would prove convenient to stimulate this intelligent way of proceeding in a logic theory machine.

30. INTRODUCTION OF NEW INDIVIDUAL PARAMETERS

Returning to point (i), we first ask the following question: to what operation in, say geometrical proof, does the introduction of individual parameters a, b, c, ... correspond? The answer is rather simple: it corresponds to the construction of auxiliary points, lines, circles, and so on. This insight has been stressed by G. Kreisel on the basis of Herbrand's Theorem [*cf.* Section 11, Theorem 21]. The same logician also made the important observation that in all known mathematical proofs the number of individual parameters involved is surprisingly small.

This observation might be construed as pointing to a rather profound difference between proof procedures as studied in formal logic and methods of proof actually applied in mathematics. But this would be a mistaken notion. The methods applied in mathematical proof differ from those which we study in formal logic only in this respect, that in mathematics, if we wish to prove a certain conclusion X on the basis of certain assumptions A_1, A_2, ..., A_m, we usually intercalate a number of lemmas L_1, L_2, ..., L_n. So we prove L_1 on the basis of the A's alone, L_2 on the basis of the A's plus L_1, and so on; finally, we prove X on the basis of all A's and all L's [*cf.* Section 11, Theorems 19 and 20]. Now it will be clear that we have to take into account the total number of all individual parameters involved in the respective proofs of these lemmas; roughly speaking, this will add up to the number of individual parameters involved in a straightforward proof of X on the basis of the A's alone.

Nevertheless, a mechanical application of the method of semantic tableaux will unavoidably result in the introduction of individual parameters which do not contribute to the closure of the tableau, and thus to a premature exhaustion of the capacity of the machine.

31. TYPES OF LOGICAL PROBLEMS

Therefore, we now return to point (ij) and we ask for devices which may prevent the machine from going into useless operations. It seems to me that, before this point can be discussed, we have to make up our mind as to the types of problems which a logical theory machine is meant to handle. As far as I see, three types of problems can be distinguished, namely:

(I) to check a given proof;

(II) to prove a given theorem on the basis of given assumptions;

(III) to discover theorems deducible from given assumptions.

Type (I) is clearly the simplest one. In this case, we have at least an estimate of the number and the kind of the individual parameters which must be introduced. By giving the machine suitable instructions, we may compel it to follow the given proof as closely as possible. If at a certain point the machine fails to reproduce the given proof, this will presumably point to a gap in the argument.

In the case of type (II), we have hardly any sound basis for an estimate of $n(U)$ and, if we simply make a guess as to its value, we still have to select those operations which are most likely to prove successful; in other words, we have to provide the machine with certain 'heuristic' devices. In this connection, I should like to offer the following suggestion. There are a number of solvable cases of the decision problem; this means, essentially, that for certain classes of formulas U a number $n(U)$ can be effectively computed. Now run a large number of formulas U through the machine, and make a statistical analysis of the distribution of those operations which prove successful and of those which are not. Then provide the machine with instructions such as to give preference to the more successful operations. This might considerably enhance the efficiency of the machine.

This statistical approach to heuristics might even be extended to the case of type (III). The danger to be avoided in this connection is clearly the production of an endless sequence of trivial theorems. Again we might try to find out, by way of statistical analysis, what operations are most likely to lead to interesting results; this would enable us to provide the machine with suitable instructions.

But it seems wiser at first not to go into problems of type (III). In my opinion, the most promising direction for a start would be to study case (I). To mention one point, it would not be necessary for the machine to reconstruct the given proof in every detail. We know at present various metamathematical results of the following kind: if a formula U is at all provable, then it has a proof of such and such a form (in fact, the method of semantic tableaux is based on such a theorem). So we may give the machine instructions such as to compel it to produce, if possible, a proof of that specific form. Nevertheless, the machine might at the same time take advantage of the results previously obtained by an analysis of the given proof.

32. CONCLUDING REMARKS

The heuristic devices, suggested in Section 31, were meant to be adapted to the specific operations of a given automatic computer. Newell and Simon and Gelernter, however, rather seem to think of those heuristic devices which are often applied by human beings in finding proofs or solving problems. It seems not unfair to draw a comparison between such devices and certain tricks to which one resorts in mental computation. A number of these tricks may be of sufficient importance to be taken into account in designing a computer (or, rather, in programming a specific problem). But many tricks, however helpful in mental computation, will be devoid of any significance with a view to computational machinery.

Similarly, there may be heuristic devices which can be simulated by a logic theory machine. One might be inclined to think in this connection of the construction of auxiliary points, lines, circles, and so on which is so often found helpful in geometrical problem solving. This, however, we have shown not to be a heuristic device in any proper sense; it is, to the contrary, an essential element in logical reasoning as such. We should rather think of heuristic devices turning up as a result of a statistical analysis as suggested in Section 31. But again many heuristic devices applied by human problem solvers will be found devoid of any significance in connection with the construction of an efficient logic theory machine.

To conclude, I should wish to mention the work of S. Kanger's collaborators, D. Prawitz, H. Prawitz, and N. Voghera (1959). On the basis of investigations by Kanger and by myself, these scientists worked out a program for an electronic computer (the Facit EDB of AB Åtvidabergs Industrier, Stockholm) which made it possibe to give the machine instructions to carry out certain deductions in elementary logic. A similar investigation was made by P. C. Gilmore (1959) on the basis of the method of semantic tableaux using the IBM 704 computer. In both cases, several relatively simple deductions were actually performed by the computer; the speed reported by Gilmore is somewhat higher than that which is mentioned by Kanger's group. For the moment, however, the speed is much too low to encourage any serious thinking about practical applications with the help of the equipment available at present. But of course, the situation may be expected to change as soon as,

(i) the methods of deduction have been more thoroughly studied and, as a result, have been simplified and refined, and,

(ij) we have at our disposal automatic computers of increased capacity and speed which are in addition more perfectly adjusted to the specific demands of a logic theory machine.

SUPPLEMENTARY EXPLANATIONS

33. FORMAL DESCRIPTION OF DEDUCTION BY CLOSED SEMANTIC TABLEAUX

Although at first the construction of deductive and semantic tableaux was presented as a heuristic device, we soon discovered that closed tableaux could conveniently be used as formal deductions. In Theorem 12 we established, in point of fact, the equivalence of the method of deduction by closed semantic tableaux to the method of classical deduction characterized in Section 5 under (D2).

However, the description of the method of deduction by tableaux, though quite adequate with respect to a heuristic device, was not by any means presented with a degree of precision comparable to the level of rigour attained in Sections 4 and 5. We shall now make up for this omission; the discussion will be confined to the case of the semantic tableaux because it is both more important and somewhat easier to handle than the case of the deductive tableaux; we only deal with implication.

(T1) A *sequent* K/L is an ordered couple of two finite (possibly empty) sets of formulas K and L; K is denoted as the *antecedent* and L as the *succedent* of the sequent K/L.

(T2) The sequent K/L is said to be *closed* if there is a formula Z which appears both in K and in L.

(T3) The sequent K/L is said to be *saturated* with respect to a formula X if one of the following conditions is fulfilled:

  (i) K/L is closed;

  (ij) X appears neither in K nor in L;

  (iij) X is an atom;

  (iv) X, or $U \rightarrow V$, is in K and either $U \in L$ or $V \in K$;

  (v) X, or $U \rightarrow V$, is in L and both $U \in K$ and $V \in L$.

(T4) The *reduction* of a sequent K/L with respect to a formula X produces:

  (i) if K/L is saturated with respect to X, the same sequent K/L;

(ij) if X, or $U \to V$, is in K, the two sequents $K/(L, U)$ and $(K, V)/L$;

(iij) if X, or $U \to V$, is in L, the sequent $(K, U)/(L, V)$. Note that a sequent produced by the reduction is at any rate saturated with respect to the formula X.

(T5) The sequent K/L is *final*, if it is saturated with respect to every formula X. Note that *every closed sequent is final*.

(T6) A *semantic tableau* for a sequent K/L is a finite sequence of sequents:

$$K_1/L_1, K_2/L_2, \ldots, K_k/L_k,$$

such that:

(i) K_1/L_1 is K/L;

(ij) for any j $(1 < j \leq k)$ we can find a formula X and an index m $(1 \leq m < j)$ such that K_j/L_j results from the reduction of K_m/L_m with respect to X;

(iij) for any j $(1 \leq j \leq k)$, either K_j/L_j is final, or we can find a formula X and (according as X appears in K_j or in L_j) two subscripts m and n $(j < m, n \leq k)$ or one subscript m $(j < m \leq k)$ such that the reduction of K_j/L_j with respect to X produces, respectively, the two sequents K_m/L_m and K_n/L_n or the sequent K_m/L_m.

(T7) A semantic tableau is *closed* if each of its final sequents is closed.

As an illustration of (T6), I offer the sequence of sequents corresponding to the semantic tableau represented by the second diagram in Section 3, *sub* (8); the last two sequents are both final and closed.

K_1/L_1: $\varnothing/[(A \to B) \to A] A$,

K_2/L_2: $(A \to B) \to A/[(A \to B) \to A] \to A, A$,

K_3/L_3: $(A \to B) \to A/[(A \to B) \to A] \to A, A, A \to B$,

K_4/L_4: $(A \to B) \to A, A/[(A \to B) \to A] \to A, A$,

K_5/L_5: $(A \to B) \to A, A/[(A \to B) \to A] \to A, A, A \to B, B$

(1) We now can establish:

Theorem 1^a. For every sequent K/L there exists a semantic tableau.

Proof. We first assign to each formula X a certain *length* $l(X)$, as follows: (i) if X is an atom, then $l(X) = 0$, (ij) $l(U \to V) = l(U) + l(V) + 1$.

123

Next we assign to each sequent K/L a *degree* $d(K/L)$, namely, the sum of the lengths of all formulas with respect to which K/L is *not* saturated.

We observe that $d(K/L) = 0$ if and only if K/L is final and that, if K'/L' results from the reduction of K/L with respect to a formula X with respect to which K/L is not saturated, we have $d(K'/L') < d(K/L)$.

Now we argue as follows. Suppose there are sequents K/L for which no semantic tableau can be found. We consider the degrees of these sequents; among these degrees there must be a *least* one, say p. Then for all sequents K/L with $d(K/L) < p$ there is a semantic tableau, but there is a certain sequent K/L with $d(K/L) = p$ for which no semantic tableau can be found.

(i) Suppose that $p = 0$. Then K/L is final, so we obtain a suitable semantic tableau by taking K/L as the only term in a sequence.

(ij) Suppose that $p > 0$. Then reduction of K/L will produce sequents K'/L' with $d(K'/L') < p$ for which, as supposed, semantic tableaux can be found. We obtain a semantic tableau for K/L by taking K/L as the first term in a sequence which includes, furthermore, those sequences which are found as semantic tableaux for the sequents K'/L'. This completes our proof.

Theorem 2ª. The problem of finding a valuation w such that $w(U) = 2$ for all formulas U in a set K and $w(V) = 0$ for all formulas V in a set L admits of a solution, if and only if the semantic tableau for the sequent K/L is not closed; each final sequent K^0/L^0 in this tableau which is not closed provides a valuation w as required.

Proof. From Section 3 we know that the valuation problem K/L is solvable if and only if at least one of the valuation problems K'/L' produced by its reduction is solvable; we also know that if a final sequent K^0/L^0 is not closed, it provides a solution of the valuation problem K^0/L^0. From this point onward, we argue as in the proof of Theorem 1^a.

It would not be difficult now to prove Theorems 5–14 in Section 5 directly, that is, without relying on theorems 1–4. In this connection, the material in Section 4 would be helpful, but I prefer not to dwell upon this matter.

124

34. INDEPENDENCE

The independence of the principles of our axiomatic construction in Section 4 can be established as follows.

(1) If we should omit *modus ponens*, then clearly only formulas X of length $l(X) > 1$ could be proved to be theses. On the other hand, for the thesis $A \to A$ we have $l(A \to A) = 1$. So *modus ponens* is independent.

(2) The independence of axiom-schema (I) is established by means of the following *pseudo-valuation* w:
(i) $w(A) = w(B) = 2$, $w(F) = 0$ for all atoms F different from A and from B;
(ij) for every formula V, $w(A \to V) = 0$, otherwise $w(U \to V)$ as usual.

We have $w(S) = 2$ for every application S of axiom-schemata (II) and (III). Moreover, if $w(U) = w(U \to V) = 2$, then $w(V) = 2$. Thus for every thesis T obtainable by *modus ponens* from axiom-schemata (II) and (III) alone, we have $w(T) = 2$. On the other hand, we have $w[B \to (A \to B)] = 0$ and hence the formula $B \to (A \to B)$ cannot be so obtained; it follows that axiom-schema (I) is independent.

(3) The independence of axiom-schema (II) is proved similarly by means of another pseudo-valuation w, namely:
(i) $w(A) = 2$, $w(B) = 0$, $w(F) = 0$ for all atoms F different from A and from B;
(ij) $w(A \to B) = 2$, otherwise $w(U \to V)$ as usual.
We find $w\{[A \to (B \to C)] \to [(A \to B) \to (A \to C)]\} = 0$.

(4) The independence of axiom-schema (III) is proved in the same way. A suitable pseudo-valuation can be obtained as follows. Each formula U admits of a unique representation:

$$U_1 \to (U_2 \to (\ldots \to (U_k \to M) \ldots)),$$

where $k = 0, 1, 2, \ldots$, and where M is an atom. If M is A or B, then

U will be called an A-formula or a B-formula, respectively. Now let w be defined as follows:

(i) $w(A) = w(B) = 0$, $w(M) = 2$ for each atom M different from A and from B;

(ij) If U is an A-formula and V is a B-formula, $w(U) = w(V) = 0$, then $w(U \rightarrow V) = 0$; otherwise $w(U \rightarrow V)$ is as usual.

It is found that:

$$w([(A \rightarrow B) \rightarrow A] \rightarrow A) = 0,$$

and that all other requirements are fulfilled.

(5) The independence of axiom-schemata (I)–(III) does not entail the independence of each single application. For instance, the formula:

$$[\{[B \rightarrow (A \rightarrow B)] \rightarrow C\} \rightarrow \{B \rightarrow (A \rightarrow B)\}] \rightarrow [B \rightarrow (A \rightarrow B)],$$

although an application of axiom-schema (III), can also be obtained by *modus ponens* from two applications of axiom-schema (I), namely:

$$\{B \rightarrow (A \rightarrow B)\} \rightarrow$$
$$\rightarrow \{[\{[B \rightarrow (A \rightarrow B)] \rightarrow C\} \rightarrow \{B \rightarrow (A \rightarrow B)\}] \rightarrow [B \rightarrow (A \rightarrow B)]\},$$

and:

$$B \rightarrow (A \rightarrow B).$$

(6) Even though we could omit certain special applications of the axiom-schemata, we could never establish all theses if of each of the axiom-schemata only finitely many applications were available. This follows immediately from the obvious fact that there is no finite upper bound for the length $l(T)$ of a thesis T.

Theorem 3ᵃ. The above principles of purely implicational logic, namely, the axiom-schemata (I)–(III) and *modus ponens*, are independent.

In a similar manner we could establish the independence of the principles of the more advanced parts of logic, but I shall not dwell upon this point.

35. INTUITIONISTIC LOGIC AND MINIMAL CALCULUS

Without establishing any close connections between deductive tableaux and intuitionistic conceptions about the nature of mathematical reasoning, we have stated merely as a fact that closed deductive tableaux represent exactly those formal deductions which are acceptable from an intuitionistic point of view. An equivalent axiomatic treatment of intuitionistic formal reasoning could be based on axiom-schemata (I) and (II) together with *modus ponens*. In Theorems 2–5 we summed up the results of this discussion which, however, was only concerned with purely implicational (intuitionistic) logic.

If we wish to develop intuitionistic sentential logic beyond this narrow domain we shall, of course, try to duplicate the discussion in Section 7. An attempt to set up an intuitionistic substitute for Kalmar's and Henkin's device would, however, involve us in a preliminary discussion about the intuitionistic criteria for the validity of logical formulas. In order to avoid this complication, we shall proceed in a different manner. It should be emphasized that our discussion here has a purely heuristic character.

On account of Kalmár's and Henkin's device, reduction schema (v^b) for negation would be replaced by the axiom-schema:

$$(U \to Z) \to [(\bar{U} \to Z) \to Z].$$

However, the application of this axiom-schema presupposes that the formula $\bar{U}$ has made its appearance in a right column. And we know that then, in the intuitionistic case, it supplants the formula Z [*cf.* Section 3, *sub* (8)]. Therefore, we should rather take:

$$(U \to \bar{U}) \to [(\bar{U} \to \bar{U}) \to \bar{U}],$$

which formula is, by purely implicational intuitionistic logic, equivalent to:

$$(U \to \bar{U}) \to \bar{U}.$$

By this and similar considerations, we obtain the following axiom-schemata for intuitionistic sentential logic:

(I^i) $U \to (V \to U)$,

(II^i) $[U \to (V \to W)] \to [(U \to V) \to (U \to W)]$,

127

(III[i]) $(U \to Z) \to [(V \to Z) \to \{(U \lor V) \to Z\}]$,
(IV[i]) $U \to (U \lor V)$,
(V[i]) $V \to (U \lor V)$,
(VI[i]) $(U \& V) \to U$,
(VII[i]) $(U \& V) \to V$,
(VIII[i]) $U \to [V \to (U \& V)]$,
(IX[i]) $U \to (\bar{U} \to Z)$,
(X[i]) $(U \to \bar{U}) \to \bar{U}$.

If we wish to have an axiom system for classical sentential logic, it is sufficient to add the axiom-schema for Peirce's Law:

$$[(U \to V) \to U] \to U .$$

For classical logic, we stated in Theorem 16 the possibility of a simplification which consists in taking, for instance, implication and negation as primitive sentential connectives and defining all other sentential connectives in terms of these two. With respect to intuitionistic logic, however, implication, disjunction, conjunction, and negation are independent primitives; that is, none of them can be defined in terms of the others. Thus, in the intuitionistic case there seems to be no immediate counterpart to Theorem 16.

This is a suitable point at which to mention the so-called *minimal calculus* (I. Johansson 1936), a logical system still weaker than intuitionistic logic. As far as implication and negation are concerned, it is obtained if, in addition to the closure and reduction schemata (i), (ij[aI]), and (ij[b]), we adopt the reduction schemata:

	Premisses	Conclusions		Premisses	Conclusions
	K'	$\varnothing$		K	$\bar{Y}$
	$\bar{U}$		(v[bM])	Y	$\varnothing$
(v[aM])		U			

In an axiomatic construction of this system we need, in addition to the axiom-schemata (I) and (II), the axiom-schema:

$$(IX^M) \quad (Y \to U) \to (\bar{U} \to \bar{Y}) .$$

In the minimal calculus, the principle: *ex falso sequitur quodlibet* holds only in the weakened form:

$$U \to (\bar{U} \to \bar{Y}) .$$

36. PROOF OF GENTZEN'S 'HAUPTSATZ'

We observed in Section 14 that in elementary logic the construction of a semantic tableau may involve an infinite regress and thus may create situations which are not, in general, amenable to an analysis by purely finitistic methods. To a certain extent, however, this difficulty can be overcome if, instead of the construction as a whole, we examine its successive stages. These stages are determined by fixing certain convenient 'stops' in the construction; this can be done as follows.

Let us denote as a *semantic tableau of rank* P for a given sequent K/L [as in Section 15, *sub* (2), we suppose the formulas in K and in L *not to contain any numerals*], a tableau constructed in accordance with rules (a)–(d) in Section 15, *sub* (3), with the understanding that formulas $(v_q) U_q(v_q)$ shall be 'treated' only if $q \leq P$ and that, apart from 1^*, numerals shall be introduced only under schema (vi^b). It follows that in the course of the construction only numerals i^*, $i \leq s(P)$, can appear.

(1) Now suppose that the semantic tableau of rank P for the sequent K/L is *not* closed. Then each non-closed subtableau provides us with a partial valuation w such that $w(U) = 2$ for every formula U in K and $w(V) = 0$ for every formula V in L and that, moreover:
(a) for *all relevant* formulas $(v_q) U_q(v_q)$, $q \leq P$, and for *all relevant* numerals k^*, $k \leq s(P)$, we have: (i) if $w[(v_q) U_q(v_q)] = 2$, then $w[U_q(k^*)] = 2$; (ij) if $w[(v_q)U_q(v_q)] = 0$, then $w[U_q(s^*(q))] = 0$.

(2) This observation suggests the introduction of the following definition. A *valuation of rank* P is a partial valuation w such that:
(b) for *all* formulas $(v_q) U_q(v_q)$, $q \leq P$, and for *all* numerals k^*, $k \leq s(P)$, the above conditions (i) and (ij) are satisfied.
We then clearly have:

Theorem 4^a. If there is a closed semantic tableau for the sequent K/L, then, for a certain natural number P, there can be no valuation w of rank P (or of any higher rank) such that $w(U) = 2$ for every formula U in K and $w(V) = 0$ for every formula V in L.

Proof. Let P be the largest of all natural numbers q such that $(v_q) U_q(v_q)$

129

is 'treated' in the given tableau. Then, if in the given tableau each numeral k^* whose introduction was not prompted by an application of reduction schema (vi^b) is replaced by 1^*, we obtain a closed semantic tableau of rank P, showing that no valuation w as described can be found.

(3) It demands somewhat more deliberation to establish:

Theorem 5ᵃ. If the semantic tableau of rank P for the sequent K/L is *not* closed, then we can find a valuation w of rank P such that $w(U) = 2$ for every formula U in K and $w(V) = 0$ for every formula V in L.

Proof. By our observation under (1), we have a partial valuation w which satisfies the above conditions (i) and (ij) for part of the formulas $(v_q) U_q(v_q)$ and for part of the numerals k^* and $s^*(q)$ involved. Let $(v_q) U_q(v_q)$, $q \leqq P$, be the first formula to be taken into account.
This formula as well as its components $U_q(j^*)$ may contain numerals k^* not previously considered. In computing truth values, such numerals are replaced by 1^*. Formulas $(v_r) U_r(v_r)$ with $r > P$ will be treated as atoms; these as well as other atoms A not previously considered are given the truth value $w(A) = 0$.
Now $w[(v_q) U_q(v_q)]$ is computed as follows:
 (i) $w(X \to Y)$ and $w(\bar{X})$ are obtained as usual,
 (ij) $w[(v)V(v)] = 2$ if $w[V(k^*)] = 2$ for all numerals k^* considered so far [it does not matter whether or not the 'new' numerals k^* are taken into account, since in any case we have $w[V(k^*)] = w[V(1^*)]!$] ; otherwise $w[(v)V(v)] = 0$.
Since $(v_q) U_q(v_q)$ was not previously considered and since $s(q)$ exceeds every k such that k^* appears in $(v_q) U_q(v_q)$, $s^*(q)$ was neither previously considered nor involved in the computation of $w[(v_q) U_q(v_q)]$. Therefore, the truth values of formulas $V(s^*(q))$ can now be adjusted as follows:
 (i) if $w[(v_q) U_q(v_q)] = 2$, then $w[V(s^*(q))] = w[V(1^*)]$; we thus obtain $w[U_q(s^*(q))] = w[U_q(1^*)] = 2$;
 (ij) if $w[(v_q) U_q(v_q)] = 0$, then $w[V(s^*(q))] = w[V(k^*)]$, where k is the smallest number such that $w[U_q(k^*)] = 0$; in this manner we obtain $w[U_q(s^*(q))] = w[U_q(k^*)] = 0$.
It will be clear that in this manner, treating one by one all formulas $(v_r) U_r(v_r)$ involved, we finally obtain a partial valuation w as required.

130

(4) From Theorems 4^a and 5^a we immediately obtain:

Theorem 6^a. A formula X is a tautology if and only if we can find a natural number P such that $w(X) = 2$ under every valuation w of rank P of of higher rank.

(5) It is now easy to prove:

Theorem 20 (Gentzen, 1934). If semantic tableaux for the sequents K/X and $(K, X)/X \to Y$ are closed, then there is also a closed semantic tableau for the sequent K/Y.

Proof. Suppose the semantic tableaux of ranks P and Q, respectively, for K/X and $(K, X)/X \to Y$ to be closed, whereas the semantic tableau of rank $P + Q$ for K/Y is not closed. This last tableau provides us with a valuation w of rank $P + Q$ such that $w(U) = 2$ for all formulas U in K and that $w(Y) = 0$. Now either (i) $w(X) = 2$ or (ij) $w(X) = 0$.
ad (i) In this case, we have $w(U) = 2$ for every formula U in (K, X) whereas $w(X \to Y) = 0$. This is inconsistent with the fact that a semantic tableau of rank $Q \leq P + Q$ for the sequent $(K, X)/X \to Y$ is closed.
ad (ij) In this case, we have $w(U) = 2$ for every formula U in K whereas $w(X) = 0$. This is inconsistent with the fact that a semantic tableau of rank $P \leq P + Q$ for the sequent K/X is closed.
Since both suppositions (i) and (ij) have been refuted, it follows that the semantic tableau of rank $P + Q$ for the sequent K/Y is closed.
Remark. The above argument holds only under the supposition that no numerals (no parameters) appear in K, X, or Y. Therefore, it is important to show that nevertheless we now have a sufficient basis for completing the proof of Theorem 21.

Theorem 7^a. If $U(p, q)$ and $U(p, q) \to V(q, r)$ are tautologies, then $V(q, r)$ is also a tautology.

Proof. By the argument *ad* (ij^0) in the (incomplete) proof of Theorem 21, the formulas $(x)(y) U(x, y)$ and $(x)(y)(z)[U(x, y) \to V(y, z)]$ are tautologies. Thus the semantic tableaux for the sequents $\emptyset/(x)(y) U(x, y)$ and $\emptyset/(x)(y)(z)[U(x, y) \to V(y, z)]$ are closed.

131

Moreover, we find by an easy construction that the semantic tableau for the sequent:

$$(x)(y)\, U(x, y),\ (x)(y)(z)[U(x, y) \to V(y, z)]/(y)(z)V(y, z)$$

is also closed. We can now apply Theorem 20 twice in the special form in which it has just been established and find that $(y)(z)V(y, z)$ is a tautology; it follows that $V(q, r)$ is a tautology.

(6) In the same manner we prove the general version of Theorem 20. Let $U(p, q, r, s)$ be the conjunction of all formulas in K and let X and Y be, respectively, $X(a, b, q, s)$ and $Y(b, c, r, s)$. Then we first show that:

$$(x)(y)(z)(t)(u)(v)[U(x, y, z, t) \to X(u, v, y, t)]$$

and:

$$(x)(y)(z)(t)(u)(v)(w)[U(x,\ y,\ z,\ t) \to \{X(u,\ v,\ y,\ t) \to Y(v,\ w,\ z,\ t)\}]$$

are tautologies. It then follows, as above, that:

$$(x)(y)(z)(t)(v)(w)[U(x, y, z, t) \to Y(v, w, z, t)]$$

is a tautology. Hence the semantic tableau for the sequent K/Y must be closed.

37. ELEMENTARY LOGIC WITH EQUALITY AND TERMS

Already in Section 13, *sub* (1), and in particular in Theorem 24, we have met with a variant to elementary logic with equality and functionality which can be denoted as elementary logic with equality and terms. As this system is actually applied in Chapter VI, it will be necessary to study it in detail.

(1) The stipulations in Section 8, as expanded in Section 12, *sub* (2), and in Section 13, must be adjusted as follows.

(T1) All individual parameters $a, b, c, \ldots, p, p', p'', \ldots$ and all parameters for individual constants $h, h', h'', \ldots$ shall be terms.

(T2) If $t, t', t'', \ldots$ are terms, then
$$g(t), g(t'), g(t''), \ldots, g'(t), g'(t'), \ldots, g''(t), \ldots,$$
$$f(t, t), f(t, t'), \ldots, f(t', t), \ldots, f(t', t'), \ldots,$$
shall be terms.

132

(T3)   Nothing shall be a term, except on the strength of (T1) and (T2).
(F1)   All *atoms*:

$A, B, C, D, \ldots,$

$A'(t), B'(t), C'(t), \ldots,$

$A''(t, t'), B''(t, t'), \ldots, t = t',$

$A'''(t, t', t''), \ldots,$

shall be formulas, provided t, t', t'' be terms.

Stipulations (F2) and (F3) are not affected.

(2) In applications of reduction schema (vi^a) we now admit, in addition to the formulas $U(p)$, all formulas $U(t)$, where t is any term obtained from parameters $p, p', p'', \ldots$ appearing in K', L, or $(v) U(v)$ by applying those function parameters which also appear in K', L, or $(v) U(v)$. In reduction schema (vi^b), however, we require as before the introduction of a '*fresh*' individual parameter.

Similar remarks apply to reduction schemata (vij^a) and (vij^b).

(3) Axiom-schema (XIII) for general quantification is replaced by:

(XIII') $(v) U(v) \to U(t) \, .$

The functionality axioms (XXI) become redundant. The equality and extensionality axioms (XVII)–(XX), however, are used in the same manner as before in the development of deductive theories. For a concrete example, see Remark preceding Theorem 14^a.

(4) The proofs of the weak completeness theorems as given in Section 11 remain unchanged.

(5) In the discussion in Section 15, however, the following modifications are required.

(i) It would prove extremely awkward to maintain the identification of the parameters $a, b, c, \ldots$ with the numerals $1^*, 2^*, 3^*, \ldots$. Instead we may associate with each term t a characteristic number (or Gödel number) c_t. Let us denote t as k^* whenever we have $c_t = k$. The definition of the function s must be adjusted in a manner such that the term $s^*(k)$ is always an individual parameter p.

(ij) Stipulation (b) in Section 15, *sub* (3), may then be adjusted as follows. In an application of reduction schema (vi^a) we not only use those terms k^* which already appear in the relevant subtableau, but also those further terms which can be obtained from these terms k^* by applying again and again those function parameters which appear in K', L, and $(v) U(v)$, insofar as for these terms t we have $c_t < k$.

It is easy to see that these modifications will permit us to restate the argument in Section 15, *sub* (4)–(7), as well as in Section 16. We thus obtain:

Theorem 8^a. The Theorems 26–30 for elementary logic hold as well for elementary logic with equality and terms.

Moreover, we have a suitable basis for restating the argument in Section 28, and so we have:

Theorem 9^a. Theorem 20 (Gentzen, 1934) and Theorem 21 (Herbrand, 1930) for elementary logic hold as well for elementary logic with equality and terms.

Thus elementary logic with equality and terms has, *grosso modo*, the same metamathematical properties as elementary logic. At the same time, however, it has considerable practical advantages.

38. THE 'TREE THEOREM' AND ITS ROLE IN THE COMPLETENESS PROOF

In Section 15, *sub* (3), I committed a fallacy when, in describing the subcases (II^a–c), I tacitly assumed that no other subcases could exist. I shall now justify this assumption by stating and proving the so-called Tree Theorem and by pointing out its importance for our completeness proof. In this manner the results obtained in Sections 15 and 16 will be established more firmly.

(1) The general structure of a semantic tableau can be characterized most strikingly by means of a *tree*. The left diagram below represents

134

the tree which corresponds to the semantic tableau in Section 14, *sub* (2).
The numbering of the points corresponds to the numbering of the
formulas in the tableau.

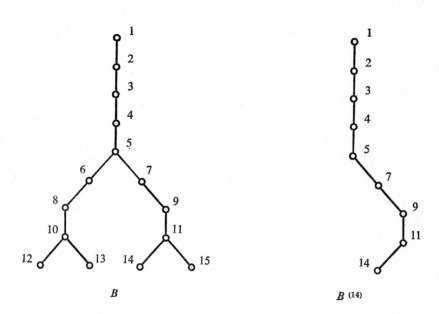

In constructing the tree which corresponds to a given semantic tableau,
we represent each formula in the tableau by a point; we disregard the
distinction between the two columns, but we represent each splitting
into subtableaux by a bifurcation in the tree. If a subtableau contains
only finitely many formulas, then it is represented by a finite branch
which has an endpoint.

(2) We wish to establish:

Theorem 10ᵃ. If a tree B contains infinitely many points, then it has a
branch which goes on indefinitely.

Proof. For every point P on B, we consider the partial configuration

135

$B^{(P)}$ which consists of all points Q which are contained in some branch on B that passes through P. It is easy to show that $B^{(P)}$ is always a tree; we have, of course, $B^{(1)} = B$. [The right diagram above shows the subtree $B^{(14)}$ of the tree represented in the left diagram. Note that 14 is not an endpoint in B; so $B^{(14)}$ goes on beyond 14 and there it shows the same bifurcations as B itself.]

Now we distinguish two kinds of points P on B: P will be *of the first kind*, if $B^{(P)}$ contains only finitely many points, and P will be *of the second kind*, if the number of points on $B^{(P)}$ is infinite. The points P of the second kind form a partial configuration B^* on B. It is easy to show that B^* is again a tree, and that a point P on B^* can never be an endpoint.

If the number of points on B is finite, then B^* does not contain any point. But if a tree $B = B^{(1)}$ contains infinitely many points, then the point 1 is clearly of the second kind. It follows that 1 is on B^* and that, as B^* contains no endpoint, there must start in 1 a branch on B^* which goes on indefinitely. This branch clearly belongs to B as well. So we have proved our Theorem.

From Theorem 10ᵃ we easily obtain

Theorem 11ᵃ. If a semantic tableau is not closed, then we have one of the subcases (IIᵃ⁻ᶜ) which were mentioned in Section 15, *sub* (3).

Proof. If the given semantic tableau contains only finitely many formulas, we clearly have subcase (IIᵃ).

Now suppose that the tableau contains infinitely many formulas. Then the corresponding tree contains infinitely many points and so, by Theorem 10ᵃ, it has a branch which goes on indefinitely. This branch may result from finitely many successive bifurcations in B; then it represents a subtableau of the given tableau in accordance with subcase (IIᵇ). Otherwise it results from infinitely many successive bifurcations in B, and then it represents a string of 'nested' subtableaux in accordance with subcase (IIᶜ).

Remark. The description of the subcases given here does not entirely agree with the description in Section 15. However, this does not matter for the proofs of Theorems 26–30.

136

39. SEMANTIC RULES FOR QUANTIFICATION THEORY

In Section 9 and in Section 15, *sub* (5) we founded our argument on a certain *hermeneutics*. We shall now explain how this 'intuitive' basis can be replaced by precise semantic rules.

(1) Suppose we are concerned with a certain set of formulas of elementary logic containing a certain binary predicate parameter A, a certain unary predicate parameter B, and a certain binary function parameter f. Let $\mathbf{M} = \; <\mathbf{S}, \mathbf{A}, \mathbf{B}, \mathbf{f}>$ be a structure consisting of a non-empty set $\mathbf{S}$ of natural numbers and of a binary predicate $\mathbf{A}$, a unary predicate $\mathbf{B}$, and a binary function $\mathbf{f}$ which are defined for elements of $\mathbf{S}$.

With each numeral n^* ($n = 0, 1, 2, \ldots$), we associate a value $w(n^*)$ in $\mathbf{S}$ in a manner such that each element of $\mathbf{S}$ appears at least once as a value. [This can be accomplished, for instance, as follows: (a) if $n \in \mathbf{S}$ then $w(n^*) = n$; (b) otherwise, $w(n^*) = k$, where k is the smallest element in $\mathbf{S}$.]

(2) The data required under (1) determine a valuation w of all formulas under consideration in accordance with the following semantic rules:

(S0) $w[A(m^*, n^*)] = 2$ if $w(m^*)$ has the relation $\mathbf{A}$ to $w(n^*)$; otherwise, $w[A(m^*, n^*)] = 0$. $w[B(m^*)] = 2$ if $w(m^*)$ has the property $\mathbf{B}$; otherwise, $w[B(m^*)] = 0$; $w[f(m^*, n^*) = p^*] = 2$, if $\mathbf{f}[w(m^*), w(n^*)] = w(p^*)$; otherwise, $w[f(m^*, n^*) = p^*] = 0$.

Rule (S1) in Section 7 remains unchanged.

(S2) $w[(v) U(v)] = 2$ if, for each natural number n, $w[U(n^*)] = 2$; otherwise, $w[(v) U(v)] = 0$. $w[(Ev) U(v)] = 2$ if, for at least one natural number n, $w[U(n^*)] = 2$; otherwise, $w[(Ev) U(v)] = 0$.

If n runs through *all* natural numbers $0, 1, 2, \ldots$, then n^* runs through *all* numerals and, by virtue of the condition imposed upon w, $w(n^*)$ runs through *all* elements of $\mathbf{S}$ (possibly with repetitions) and takes no value outside $\mathbf{S}$. For this reason, rules (S0) and (S2) are appropriate. If $\mathbf{S}$ is not a set of natural numbers, then the conditions imposed upon w and the rules (S0) and (S2) must be restated. No difficulties arise so long as $\mathbf{S}$ remains finite or denumerably infinite. Note that at any rate $\mathbf{S}$ must be non-empty.

(3) It is easy to see that the construction in Section 15, *sub* (4)–(5), and in Section 16, *sub* (1)–(2) entirely answers the above semantic rules (S0–2). We intended to construct a valuation w such that $w(U) = 2$ for every U in K and $w(V) = 0$ for every V in L. With this purpose in mind, we first determined the values $w(n^*)$ and thus at the same time constructed a suitable non-empty set S of natural numbers. Then we determined the truth values $w(X)$ for the atomic formulas X and at the same time constructed suitable predicates A and B as well as a suitable function f. Finally, we determined the truth values $w(Y)$ for compound formulas Y and showed that for the formulas in K and in L the above conditions were satisfied.

(4) Conversely, we can now see that the reduction schemata (vi^a) and (vi^b) in Section 9 and (vij^a) and (vij^b) in Section 11, *sub* (1) fully answer the corresponding clauses in rule (S2).

(5) The fact that only structures M are considered in which S is a set of natural numbers is, of course, a rather serious restriction. It is, however, not very difficult to see how the above set of semantic rules could be generalized. And, moreover, it follows from our results that in the context of our present work there is hardly any need for structures of a more general kind. For in all those cases in which the existence of certain structures could be reasonably anticipated, we were able to establish the existence of suitable structures of the above special kind.

40. DEDUCTION-THEORETIC TREATMENT OF THE THEORY OF QUANTIFICATION

In Section 2, we discussed a purely deduction-theoretic approach to the problems of logic. Later on, in Section 5, *sub* (6), and in Section 10 we introduced a notion of (classical) deducibility based upon our axiomatic approach to logical theory. As explained at the end of Section 6, this step permits us to disregard the purely deduction-theoretic approach.

I now wish to show that nevertheless a purely deduction-theoretic treatment is possible of the more advanced parts of classical logic even though, at first, the deduction-theoretic approach leads to intuitionistic

138

rather than to classical logic. In fact, the basis for such a treatment was laid in Section 3, *sub* (10)–(11). The result of the discussion there can now be formulated as follows. If for negation we introduce as an additional schema:

	True	False
	K	L'
		Z
(v^c)	$\overline{}$	
	Z	

then the formula Z can be protected against the effects of its being supplanted by a formula Y appearing in the right column later on. For, if an application of this schema has been intercalated, then the formula Z, in spite of its being supplanted, can be reintroduced any time into the right column by an application of schema (v^a).

Thus the semantic tableau can be *formally* regarded as a deductive tableau to the extent that it can be immediately rewritten as a formal deduction in accordance with *classical* logic. As a first example I refer to the formal deduction of Peirce's Law in Section 3, *sub* (11).

(1) Let us now consider the semantic tableau for the sequent:

$$\emptyset / (A \to C) \to [(B \to C) \to \{[(A \to B) \to B] \to C\}],$$

namely:

True			False		
			(1)	$(A \to C) \to [\ldots]$	
(2)	$A \to C$		(3)	$(B \to C) \to \{\ldots\}$	
(4)	$B \to C$		(5)	$[(A \to B) \to B] \to C$	
(6)	$(A \to B) \to B$		(7)	C	
	(9)	C	(8)	B	
	(11)	B	(10)	$A \to B$	
(12)	A		(13)	B	
	(15)	C	(14)	A	

139

From rewriting this tableau as it stands, no sensible formal deduction results. This is due to the fact that one of the subtableaux has been closed because of the appearance of formulas (7) and (15) irrespective of the circumstance that, in accordance with the closure rules for deductive tableaux, formula (7) is supplanted in this subtableau by formula (8). Thus the above tableau cannot be considered, even formally, as a deductive tableau, and so we have no reason to expect that its being rewritten will produce a formal deduction. This defect can be made up for by suitable applications of schemata (v^c) and (v^a).

True			False		
(2)	$A \rightarrow C$		(1)	$(A \rightarrow C) \rightarrow [\ldots]$	
(4)	$B \rightarrow C$		(3)	$(B \rightarrow C) \rightarrow \{\ldots\}$	
(6)	$(A \rightarrow B) \rightarrow B$		(5)	$[(A \rightarrow B) \rightarrow B] \rightarrow C$	
(7')	$\bar{C}$		(7)	C	
		(9) $\quad C$	(8)	B	
		(11) $\quad B$	(10)	$A \rightarrow B$	
(12)	A		(13)	B	
		(15) $\quad C$	(14)	A	(7'') $\quad C$

This tableau can be readily rewritten so as to produce the following formal deduction:

(2)	$A \rightarrow C$	[+ hyp 1]
(4)	$B \rightarrow C$	[+ hyp 2]
(6)	$(A \rightarrow B) \rightarrow B$	[+ hyp 3]
(7')	$\bar{C}$	[+ hyp 4]
(12)	A	[+ hyp 5]
(15)	C	(2), (12)
(13)	B	(7'), (15)
(10)	$A \rightarrow B$	[− hyp 5]

(8)	B		(6), (10)
(7)	C	(4), (8)	$[-\text{ hyp } 4]$
(5)	$[(A \rightarrow B) \rightarrow B] \rightarrow C$		$[-\text{ hyp } 3]$
(3)	$(B \rightarrow C) \rightarrow \{\ldots\}$		$[-\text{ hyp } 2]$
(1)	$(A \rightarrow C) \rightarrow [\ldots]$		$[-\text{ hyp } 1]$

(2) Another example is provided by *Plato's Law*:

$$\emptyset/(Ex)[(Ey)A(y) \rightarrow A(x)],$$

which produces the following semantic tableau:

True		False	
		(1)	$(Ex)[(Ey)A(y) \rightarrow A(x)]$
		(2)	$(Ey)A(y) \rightarrow A(a)$
(3)	$(Ey)A(y)$	(4)	$A(a)$
(5)	$A(b)$	(6)	$(Ey)A(y) \rightarrow A(b)$
(7)	$(Ey)A(y)$	(8)	$A(b)$

In this tableau the formula (1) is supplanted by formula (2), and thus in a deductive tableau the appearance of formula (6) would not be justified. So we have to intercalate applications of schemata (v^c) and (v^a) as follows.

	True		False	
(v^c)			(1)	$(Ex)[(Ey)A(y) \rightarrow A(x)]$
	(1')	$(Ex)[(Ey)A(y) \rightarrow A(x)]$	(2)	$(Ey)A(y) \rightarrow A(a)$
(v^a)	(3)	$(Ey)A(y)$	(4)	$A(a)$
	(5)	$A(b)$	(1'')	$(Ex)[(Ey)A(y) \rightarrow A(x)]$
			(6)	$(Ey)A(y) \rightarrow A(b)$
	(7)	$(Ey)A(y)$	(8)	$A(b)$

Rewriting this tableau, we obtain the following formal deduction:

(1')	$(Ex)[(Ey)A(y) \rightarrow A(x)]$	$[+\text{ hyp } 1]$
(3)	$(Ey)A(y)$	$[+\text{ hyp } 2]$
(5)	$A(b)$	$[+\text{ hyp } 3]$
(7)	$(Ey)A(y)$	$[+\text{ hyp } 4]$

(8)	$A(b)$	(5)
(6)	$(Ey)A(y) \to A(b)$	[— hyp 4]
(1″)	$(Ex)[(Ey)A(y) \to A(x)]$	[— hyp 3]
(4)	$A(a)$	(1′), (1″)
(2)	$(Ey)A(y) \to A(a)$	[— hyp 2]
(1)	$(Ex)[(Ey)(Ay) \to A(x)]$	[— hyp 1]

The way in which hypothesis 3 is eliminated deserves some special attention. The step from formula (6) to formula (1″) is obvious. We now observe that formula (1″) no longer contains the parameter b. Therefore, even though hypothesis 3 has been used in deducing formula (1″), the value of b is no longer relevant. Thus, as regards formula (1″), hypothesis 3 can be replaced by formula (3) and hence hypothesis 3 becomes superfluous.

(3) Our last illustration will be:

$$\emptyset/(x)[A \lor B(x)] \to \{A \lor (y)B(y)\},$$

which produces the following semantic tableau.

True		False	
		(1) $(x)[\ldots] \to \{A \lor (y)B(y)\}$	
(2) $(x)[A \lor B(x)]$		(3) $A \lor (y)B(y)$	
		(4) A	
		(5) $(y)B(y)$	
(7) $A \lor B(a)$		(6) $B(a)$	
(8) A	(9) $B(a)$		

Since in this tableau formulas (3) and (4) are supplanted, we consider instead:

True		False	
		(1) $(x)[\ldots] \to \{A \lor (y)B(y)\}$	
(2) $(x)[A \lor B(x)]$		(3) $A \lor (y)B(y)$	
(3′) $A \lor (y)B(y)$		(4) A	
(4′) $\bar{A}$		(3″) $A \lor (y)B(y)$	
		(5) $(y)B(y)$	
(7) $A \lor B(a)$		(6) $B(a)$	
(8) A	(9) $B(a)$	(4″) A	

and so obtain the formal deduction:

(2)	$(x)[A \vee B(x)]$	$[+ \text{ hyp } 1]$
(3′)	$\overline{A \vee (y)B(y)}$	$[+ \text{ hyp } 2]$
(4′)	$\bar{A}$	$[+ \text{ hyp } 3]$
(7)	$A \vee B(a)$	(2)
(4″)	A	$[+ \text{ hyp } 4]$
(9)	$B(a)$	(4′), (4″)
(6)	$B(a)$	$[- \text{ hyp } 4]$
(5)	$(y)B(y)$	(6)
(3″)	$A \vee (y)B(y)$	(5)
(4)	A	$[- \text{ hyp } 3]$
(3)	$A \vee (y)B(y)$	(4) $[- \text{ hyp } 2]$
(1)	$(x)[\ldots] \rightarrow \{A \vee (y)B(y)\}$	$[- \text{ hyp } 1]$

Here the elimination of hypothesis 4 deserves special attention. Having inferred formula (9) from (4′) and (4″) by the principle that *ex falso sequitur quodlibet*, we observe that, as regards this conclusion, hypothesis 4 can be replaced by formula (7) which states, as alternatives, this hypothesis and the desired conclusion.

Hypothesis 4 being eliminated, conclusion (6) no longer depends on any hypothesis involving the parameter *a*. Thus (5) can be obtained by generalizing formula (6).

(4) It will be clear that starting from a closed semantic tableau and intercalating suitable applications of schemata (vᶜ) and (vᵃ), we can always obtain a formal deduction of a type which, besides being based on the principles of classical logic, reflects our 'intuitive' conceptions regarding deductive reasoning. These deductions proceed in accordance with a certain *system of natural deduction* which agrees with ideas first set forth by Gentzen and Jaskowski (*cf.* Section 6). As far as implication, negation, and generalization are concerned, the rules for our particular version are contained in schemata (i), (ijᵃᴵ), (ijᵇ), (vᵃ), (vᵇ), (vᶜ), (viᵃ), and (viᵇ). In order to facilitate comparison with other versions, I now restate these rules as follows:

(i)	(ij^{aI})	(ij^b)	(v^a)
K'	K'	K	K'
Z	$U \to V, U$	U	$U, \bar{U}$
Z	V	V	V
		$U \to V$	

(v^b)	(v^c)	(vi^a)	(vi^b)
K	K	K'	K
U	$\bar{U}$	$(v)U(v)$	$[U(p)]$
$\bar{U}$	U	$U(p)$	$(v)U(v)$
$\bar{U}$	U		

In each of these rules, we mean to state that the last formula follows from a certain set of premisses which is (K', Z) for rule (i), $(K', U \to V, U)$ for rule (ij^{aI}), $(K', U, \bar{U})$ for rule (v^a), $(K', (v)U(v))$ for rule (vi^a), and K for all other rules.

In rules (i), (ij^{aI}), v^a), and (vi^a), the statement is not affected by any special assumptions. In rule (vi^b), it is assumed that $U(p)$ follows from K; moreover, the parameter p must not appear in K.

In rule (ij^b), it is assumed that V follows from (K, U), in rule (v^b), that $\bar{U}$ follows from (K, U), and in rule (v^c), that U follows from $(K, \bar{U})$; thus these rules make provision for the elimination of hypotheses previously introduced. In the case of rules (v^b) and (v^c), the relevant hypothesis U, or $\bar{U}$, is sometimes denoted as a *hypothesis for reduction*.

All the above rules except rule (v^c) are conclusive from an intuitionistic point of view. If rule (v^c) is omitted, then we obtain the intuitionistic version of our system of natural deduction.

In concluding, it is interesting to make the following observation. It is shown by our experience under (1)–(3) that in classical deduction indirect proof must be considered as a '*natural*' device even in those cases where the premisses and conclusions involved do not contain negation. For in the above classical system of natural deduction the deduction problems proposed by the sequents concerned could not be solved without reliance upon rule (v^c). This also explains why the system of *intuitionistic implicational logic*, based upon rules (i), (ij^{aI}), and (ij^b) [or, alternatively, upon axiom-schemata (I) and (II), together with *modus ponens*; *cf.* Section 5, *sub* (5)] is sometimes called *positive implicational logic*. Accordingly, this system has been characterized by Church (following Hilbert and Bernays) as the part of sentential logic 'which may be said to be independent in some sense of the existence of a negation.'

(5) The above discussion can be adapted to the case of purely implicational classical logic provided the following modifications be made. In schema (v^c) we replace $\bar{Z}$ by $Z \rightarrow Y$; let the schema which results be called (ij^{aC}). Accordingly we replace in the corresponding deduction rule (v^c) $\bar{U}$ by $U \rightarrow V$ and we denote the deduction rule thus obtained as (ij^{aC}). In the example given under (1) the formula (7') $\bar{C}$ is replaced by (7') $C \rightarrow A$; it may be left to the reader to study the tableau which results and to transform it into a formal deduction in purely implicational classical logic.

41. NUMERICAL COMPUTATION

In order to substantiate various statements made in Sections 17 and 18, the following supplementary discussion is necessary. Its importance will be more easily grasped after a first reading of the sections just mentioned. It was shown there (although the argument was fragmentary) that such deductive systems as the system A and its various extensions B were necessarily incomplete. Therefore, the question arises whether these systems really provide a basis for numerical computation. This question we shall answer in the affirmative by proving Theorem 33 as well as a few related results.

(1) In the present context, numerical computation is best conceived as a certain kind of formal deduction. We start from the following initial equations:

(C1) $$p = p;$$

(C2) $$p + 0 = p;$$

145

(C3) $$p + Sq = S(p + q);$$

(C4) $$p \cdot 0 = 0;$$

(C5) $$p \cdot Sq = p \cdot q + p;$$

(C6) $$p^0 = S0;$$

(C7) $$p^{Sq} = p^q \cdot p.$$

We apply the following inference schemata:

(C8)
$$\frac{t(p) = t'(p)}{t(t'') = t'(t'')}$$

(C9)
$$\frac{t = t'}{t' = t}$$

(C10)
$$\frac{t = t'}{St = St'}$$

(C11)
$$\frac{\begin{array}{c} t = t' \\ t' = t'' \end{array}}{t = t''}$$

(C12)
$$\frac{\begin{array}{c} t = t' \\ t'' = t''' \end{array}}{t + t'' = t' + t'''}$$

(C13)
$$\frac{\begin{array}{c} t = t' \\ t'' = t''' \end{array}}{t \cdot t'' = t' \cdot t'''}$$

(C14)
$$\frac{\begin{array}{c} t = t' \\ t'' = t''' \end{array}}{t^{t''} = t'^{t'''}}$$

146

For later use, I list:

(C15) $$0 \neq Sp$$

(C16) $$\frac{St = St'}{t = t'}$$

(C17) $$\frac{p \neq 0}{(Ey)\{p = Sy\}}$$

Theorem 12ª. The deductive system A makes allowance for the initial equations and inference schemata (C1–17), that is: all initial equations are deducible in A and, whenever the premisses in an inference schema are deducible in A (possibly under certain assumptions), so is also the conclusion (under the same assumptions).

Proof. Clearly (C1) is based on axiom (XVII), (C2) on (A2), (C3) on (A3), (C4) on (A4), (C5) on (A5), (C6) on (A6), (C7) on (A7), (C8) on (XIII), (C9) on (XVIII), (C10) and (C12–14) on (XX), (C11) on (XIX), (C15) on (A8), (C16) on (A1), and (C17) on (A9).

Theorem 13ª. Theorem 12ª can be extended to the following derived inference schemata:

(C18) $$\frac{t = t'}{t/p \cdot T = t'/p \cdot T}$$

(C19) $$\frac{\begin{array}{c} t/p \cdot T = t/p \cdot T' \\ t = t' \end{array}}{t'/p \cdot T = t'/p \cdot T'}$$

(C20) $$\frac{\begin{array}{c} p \neq 0 \\ p \neq S0 \\ \vdots \\ p \neq S_k 0 \end{array}}{(Ey)\{p = S_{k+1}y\}}$$

147

(C21)
$$\frac{p + q = k^0}{q = 0 \vee q = S0 \vee \ldots \vee q = k^0}$$

(C22)
$$\frac{p + q = k^0}{p = 0 \vee p = S0 \vee \ldots \vee p = k^0}$$

(C23)
$$\frac{\begin{array}{c} p \cdot q = k^0 \\ q \neq 0 \end{array}}{p = 0 \vee p = S0 \vee \ldots \vee p = k^0}$$

(C24)
$$\frac{\begin{array}{c} p \cdot q = k^0 \\ p \neq 0 \end{array}}{q = 0 \vee q = S0 \vee \ldots \vee q = k^0}$$

(C25)
$$\frac{\begin{array}{c} p^q = k^0 \\ q \neq 0 \end{array}}{p = 0 \vee p = S0 \vee \ldots \vee p = k^0}$$

(C26)
$$\frac{\begin{array}{c} p^q = k^0 \\ p \neq 0 \\ p \neq S0 \end{array}}{q = 0 \vee q = S0 \vee \ldots \vee q = k^0}$$

Remark. By $t/p \cdot T$ we denote the term which results if in the term T the parameter p is replaced throughout by the term t. And by $S_k t$ we denote the term $S[k - 2$ symbols $S]St$ (so $S_k 0$ is the same term as k^0).

Proof. In justifying (C18) we first observe that in Section 17, *sub* (1) it would have been proper to formulate a stipulation like (F3″) in Section 1. At any rate, if T is a term there is a finite sequence $t_1, t_2, \ldots, t_i$ such that, for any $j \leq i$, one of the following conditions is satisfied:
  (i) t_j is 0, or one of the individual parameters $a, b, \ldots$;
  (ij) t_j is St_m for some $m < j$;
  (iij) t_j is $t_m + t_n$, $t_m \cdot t_n$, or $t_m{}^{t_n}$ for some $m, n < j$,
whereas t_i is the term T. Now suppose that $t = t'$ and that for $m = 1$, $2, \ldots, j - 1$, we have $t/p \cdot t_m = t'/p \cdot t_m$.

ad (i) If t_j is 0 or an individual parameter different from p, then both $t/p \cdot t_j$ and $t'/p \cdot t_j$ are t_j; thus we have $t/p \cdot t_j = t'/p \cdot t_j$ by (C1). And if t_j is p, then $t/p \cdot t_j$ and $t'/p \cdot t_j$ are, respectively, t and t', and so we have $t/p \cdot t_j = t'/p \cdot t_j$ by our supposition.

ad (ij) If t_j is St_m, then $t/p \cdot t_j$ and $t'/p \cdot t_j$ are, respectively, $S(t/p \cdot t_m)$ and $S(t'/p \cdot t_m)$. So we have:

(C10)
$$\frac{t/p \cdot t_m = t'/p \cdot t_m}{S(t/p \cdot t_m) = S(t'/p \cdot t_m)} \qquad \text{[hyp]}$$

ad (iij) If t_j is $t_m + t_n$, then $t/p \cdot t_j$ and $t'/p \cdot t_j$ are, respectively, $(t/p \cdot t_m) + (t/p \cdot t_n)$ and $(t'/p \cdot t_n) + (t'/p \cdot t_m)$. Hence:

(C12)
$$\frac{\begin{array}{ll} t/p \cdot t_m = t'/p \cdot t_m & \text{[hyp]} \\ t/p \cdot t_n = t'/p \cdot t_n & \text{[hyp]} \end{array}}{(t/p \cdot t_m) + (t/p \cdot t_n) = (t'/p \cdot t_m) + (t'/p \cdot t_n)}$$

The two remaining cases are treated similarly by means of (C13) and (C14). So in all cases (i)–(iij) we have $t/p \cdot t_j = t'/p \cdot t_j$. It clearly follows that this holds for every $j \leqq i$. Since t_i is T, this completes our proof.

Now (C19) is established as follows:

(C18)
(C9)
$$\frac{\dfrac{t = t'}{t/p \cdot T = t'/p \cdot T}}{t'/p \cdot T = t/p \cdot T} \qquad \text{[prem]}$$

(C18)
(C11)
$$\frac{\dfrac{t/p \cdot T = t/p \cdot T'}{t/p \cdot T' = t'/p \cdot T'}}{t'/p \cdot T = t'/p \cdot T'} \qquad \text{[prem]}$$

Turning to (C20), we first consider the particular case where $k = 1$. In the general case we proceed as in the proof of (C18).

(C17)
$$\frac{\begin{array}{ll} p \neq 0 & \text{[prem]} \\ p \neq S0 & \text{[prem]} \end{array}}{\begin{array}{c}(Ey)\{p = Sy\} \\ p = Sp_1 \end{array}}$$

(C19)
$$\frac{p_1 = 0}{p = S0}$$
[hyp for red]

[abs, hence:]

(C17)
$$\frac{p_1 \neq 0}{(Ey)\{p_1 = Sy\}}$$

(C19)
$$\frac{p_1 = Sp_2}{p = SSp_2}$$

$$(Ey)\{p = SSy\}$$

In dealing with the general case, we suppose that $(Ey)\{p = S_{j+1}y\}$ has already been established. We then continue as follows:

$$p \neq 0 \qquad \text{[prem]}$$
$$p \neq S0 \qquad \text{[prem]}$$
$$\vdots$$
$$p \neq S_j0 \qquad \text{[prem]}$$
$$p \neq S_{j+1}0 \qquad \text{[prem]}$$
$$\vdots$$
$$(Ey)\{p = S_{j+1}y\}$$
$$p = S_{j+1}p_{j+1}$$

(C19)
$$\frac{p_{j+1} = 0}{p = S_{j+1}0}$$
[hyp for red]

[abs, hence:]

(C17)
$$\frac{p_{j+1} \neq 0}{(Ey)\{p_{j+1} = Sy\}}$$

(C19)
$$\frac{p_{j+1} = Sp_{j+2}}{p = S_{j+2}p_{j+2}}$$

$$(Ey)\{p = S_{j+2}y\}$$

In order to establish (C21) we suppose that $p + q = k^0$ and, in addition, $q \neq 0, q \neq S0, \ldots, q \neq S_k0$. Then by (C20) we have $(Ey)\{q = S_{k+1}y\}$; say $q = S_{k+1}r$. Then $p + S_{k+1}r = S_k0$; hence, applying (C3) $k + 1$ times, $S_{k+1}(p + r) = S_k0$ and, applying (C16) k times, $S(p + r) = 0$, which contradicts (C15).

Schema (C8) is known as the *rule of substitution* and schema (C19) as the *rule of replacing equals by equals*. These rules play an important

150

role in formal computation; their application is not always announced. *Remark.* Both proofs and further applications of the above initial equations and inference schemata are best construed as abbreviated semantic tableaux whose antecedent contains axioms (XVII)–(XX) and (A1–9) [and, possibly, additional assumptions] and whose succedent consists of the relevant conclusion; or, in other words, as formal deductions in the system of Section 40, *sub* (4). As an example we consider inference schema (C20) for $k = 1$; we observe that axiom (XX) is applied in the form:

$$(x)(y)(z)[x = y \to \{z = Sx \to z = Sy\}].$$

True	False
(XX) $(x)(y)(z)\,[x = y \to \{z = Sx \to z = Sy\}]$	$(Ey)\{p = SSy\}$ [conc]
(A9) $(x)[x = 0 \lor (Ey)\{x = Sy\}]$	$p = 0$
$\underline{p = 0}$ [prem]	$p = S0$
$\underline{p = S0}$ [prem]	
$p = 0 \lor (Ey)\{p = Sy\}$	

$p = 0$	$(Ey)\{p = Sy\}$			
	$p = Sp_1$			
$p_1 = 0 \lor (Ey)\{p_1 = Sy\}$				

$p_1 = 0$	$(Ey)\{p_1 = Sy\}$			
$p_1 = 0 \to$	$p_1 = Sp_2$		$p = SSp_2$	
$\to \{p = Sp_1 \to p = S0\}$	$p_1 = Sp_2 \to$			
	$\to \{p = Sp_1 \to p = SSp_2\}$			

$p = Sp_1 \to p = S0$	$p = Sp_1 \to p = SSp_2$	$p_1 = 0$	$p_1 = Sp_2$
$p = S0$	$p = SSp_2$	$p = Sp_1$	$p = Sp_1$

Theorem 14ᵃ. For every numerical term T we can find a unique natural number k such that $w(T) = k$ and hence $w(T = k^0) = 2$.

Proof. We proceed in the same manner as in the proof of Theorem 13ᵃ. Since T is a numerical term, t_j can be only 0 if we have case (i). Let us suppose that for the terms t_1, t_2, ..., t_{j-1}, suitable numbers k_1, k_2, ..., k_{j-1} have already been found.

151

ad (i) If t_j is the term 0, then we take $k_j = 0$; we clearly have $w(0 = 0) = 2$.
ad (ij) If t_j is St_m, $m < j$, then we take $k_j = k_m + 1$.
ad (iij) If t_j is $t_m + t_n$, $m, n < j$, then we take $k_j = k_m + k_n$, and so on.

Theorem 15ª. All formulas:

$$S(j^0) = (j + 1)^0$$

are deducible in A.

Proof. Because $S(j^0)$ is the same term as $(j + 1)^0$, this follows from (C1) by (C8).

Theorem 16ª. All formulas:

$$k^0 + l^0 = (k + l)^0$$

are deducible in A.

Proof. We proceed in the same manner as in the proof of Theorem 13ª, in connection with (C20); specifically, we show that we can successively deduce $k^0 + 0 = (k + 0)^0$, $k^0 + S0 = (k + 1)^0$, ..., $k^0 + j^0 = (k + j)^0$, ..., $k^0 + l^0 = (k + l)^0$.
(A) The formula $k^0 + 0 = (k + 0)^0$, or $k^0 + 0 = k^0$, follows from (C2).
(B) Suppose we have already deduced $k^0 + j^0 = (k + j)^0$. Then we continue as follows:

$$k^0 + j^0 = (k + j)^0 \qquad \text{[hyp]}$$
$$k^0 + (j + 1)^0 = k^0 + Sj^0 \qquad \text{[Theorem 15ª]}$$
$$k^0 + Sj^0 = S(k^0 + j^0) \qquad \text{[(C3)]}$$
$$S(k^0 + j^0) = S(k + j)^0 \qquad \text{[(C10)]}$$
$$S(k + j)^0 = (k + j + 1)^0 \qquad \text{[Theorem 15ª]}$$

(C11) $\dfrac{}{k^0 + (j + 1)^0 = (k + j + 1)^0}$

It will be clear that, starting from (A) and applying again and again the argument under (B), we shall finally arrive at the conclusion $k^0 + l^0 = (k + l)^0$.

Theorem 17ª. All formulas:

$$k^0 \cdot l^0 = (k \cdot l)^0$$

are deducible in A.

Proof. We proceed as in the proof of Theorem 16[a].

(A) The formula $k^0 \cdot 0 = (k \cdot 0)^0$, or $k^0 \cdot 0 = 0$, follows from (C4).

(B) After deducing $k^0 \cdot j^0 = (k \cdot j)^0$, we continue as follows:

$$k^0 \cdot j^0 = (k \cdot j)^0 \qquad \text{[hyp]}$$
$$k^0 \cdot (j+1)^0 = k^0 \cdot Sj^0 \qquad \text{[Theorem 15}^\text{a}\text{]}$$
$$k^0 \cdot Sj^0 = k^0 \cdot j^0 + k^0 \qquad \text{[(C5)]}$$
$$k^0 \cdot j^0 + k^0 = (k \cdot j)^0 + k^0 \qquad \text{[(C12)]}$$
$$(k \cdot j)^0 + k^0 = (k \cdot j + k)^0 \qquad \text{[Theorem 16}^\text{a}\text{]}$$
$$(k \cdot j + k)^0 = [k \cdot (j+1)]^0 \qquad \text{[(C1)]}$$

(C11)
$$\overline{k^0 \cdot (j+1)^0 = [k \cdot (j+1)]^0}$$

Theorem 18[a]. All formulas:

$$(k^0)^{l^0} = (k^l)^0$$

are deducible in A.

Proof. We proceed again as in the proofs of Theorems 16[a] and 17[a].

Theorem 19[a]. If T and k are as in Theorem 14[a], then the formula:

$$T = k^0$$

is deducible in A.

Proof. We proceed as in the proof of Theorem 14[a]. We suppose that the formulas $t_1 = k_1^0$, $t_2 = k_2^0$, ..., $t_{j-1} = k_{j-1}^0$ have already been deduced, and we show how to continue so as to deduce $t_j = k_j^0$ as well. The cases (i) and (ij) present no difficulties.

ad (iij) If t_j is $t_m + t_n$, we continue as follows:

$$t_m = k_m^0 \qquad \text{[hyp]}$$
$$t_n = k_n^0 \qquad \text{[hyp]}$$

(C12)
$$\overline{t_m + t_n = k_m^0 + k_n^0}$$

(C11)
$$k_m^0 + k_n^0 = (k_m + k_n)^0 \qquad \text{[Theorem 16}^\text{a}\text{]}$$
$$\overline{t_j = k_j^0}$$

And so on.

Theorem 20[a]. If $k \neq l$, then the formula $\overline{k^0 = l^0}$ is deducible in A.

Proof. If $k \neq l$, then the formula $\overline{k^0 = l^0}$, or $\overline{S_k 0 = S_l 0}$, is clearly deducible on the basis of (C15) and (C16).

Theorem 21ᵃ. If $m \neq w(T)$, then the formula $\overline{T = m^0}$ is deducible in A.

Proof. If $w(T) = k$, then $k \neq m$. By Theorems 19ᵃ and 20ᵃ, the formulas $T = k^0$ and $\overline{k^0 = m^0}$ are deducible in A. It follows that the formula $\overline{T = m^0}$ is also deducible in A.

Theorems 14ᵃ, 19ᵃ, and 21ᵃ clearly provide a basis for Theorem 33.

Theorem 22ᵃ. If $k - l = m$, then the formula:

$$k^0 - l^0 = m^0$$

is deducible in A.

Proof. In accordance with the definition in Section 17, *sub* (6), we have to show that the formula:

$$(x)\{l^0 + x = k^0 \leftrightarrow x = m^0\}$$

is deducible in A. This will be the case if:

$$l^0 + p = k^0 \leftrightarrow p = m^0$$

is deducible in A. Since k^0 is the same term as $(l + m)^0$, this last formula is the same as:

$$l^0 + p = (l + m)^0 \leftrightarrow p = m^0 \,.$$

(A) In order to show that the implication:

$$l^0 + p = (l + m)^0 \rightarrow p = m^0$$

is deducible in A, it is sufficient to show that by the above devices $p = m^0$ is deducible from $l^0 + p = (l + m)^0$, as follows:

(C21)	$l^0 + p = (l + m)^0$
(C18)	$\overline{p = 0 \vee p = S0 \vee \ldots \vee p = j^0 \vee \ldots \vee p = (l + m)^0}$
	$\overline{l^0 + p = l^0 + j^0}$
(C9)	$l^0 + j^0 = (l + j)^0 \qquad$ [Theorem 16ᵃ]
	$\overline{l^0 + p = (l + j)^0}$
(C11)	$(l + m)^0 = l^0 + p$
	$\overline{(l + m)^0 = (l + j)^0}$

154

By Theorem 20^a, this conclusion is refutable in A unless we have $j = m$. Thus from the above disjunction only the term $p = m^0$ remains.

(B) The proof of the implication $p = m^0 \rightarrow l^0 + p = (l + m)^0$ is very simple.

Theorem 23^a. If $k - l \neq n$, then the formula:

$$\overline{k^0 - l^0 = n^0}$$

is deducible in A. – *Cf.* Section 17, *sub* (6).

Theorem 24^a. If $k : l = m$, then the formula $k^0 : l^0 = m^0$ is deducible in A.

Theorem 25^a. If $k : l \neq n$, then the formula $\overline{k^0 : l^0 = n^0}$ is deducible in A.

The proofs of Theorems 23^a–25^a are left to the reader.

Theorem 26^a. If $m < n$, then the formula $m^0 < n^0$ is deducible in A.

Proof. In accordance with the definition in Section 18, *sub* (4), we have to show that the formula:

$$(Ez)\{m^0 + Sz = n^0\}$$

is deducible in A. This is a very simple matter.

Theorem 27^a. If $m \not< n$, then the formula $\overline{m^0 < n^0}$ is deducible in A.

Theorem 28^a. If $k = p \cdot q + r, r < p$, then the formula:

$$k^0 = p^0 \cdot q^0 + r^0 \ \& \ r^0 < p^0$$

is deducible in A.

Proof. This follows clearly from Theorems 19^a and 26^a.

Theorem 29^a. If the formula in Theorem 28^a is false, then its negation is deducible in A.

Theorem 30^a. If A is the representing number of the finite sequence $a_1, a_2, \ldots, a_k$, then the formulas:

$$[A^0]_O = k^0, [A^0]_{SO} = a_1^0, [A^0]_{SSO} = a_2^0, \ldots, [A^0]_{k^0} = a_k^0$$

155

and:

$$(x)(y)\{[A^0]_y = x \leftrightarrow [(x = k^0 \ \& \ y = 0) \lor (x = a_1^0 \ \& \ y = S0) \lor$$
$$\lor (x = a_2^0 \ \& \ y = SS0) \lor \ldots \lor (x = a_k^0 \ \& \ y = k^0)]\}$$

are deducible in A.

Theorem 31ª. If A is *not* the representing number of the finite sequence $a_1, a_2, \ldots, a_k$, then those of the aforementioned formulas which are false are refutable in A.

Theorem 32ª. If $n! = m$, then the formulas $(n!)^0 = m^0$ and:

$$(t)[(Ez)\{[z]_0 = n^0 \ \& \ [z]_1 = 1 \ \& \ (u)(v)[(0 < u \ \& \ u < n^0 \ \&$$
$$\& \ [z]_u = v) \to [z]_{Su} = Su \cdot v] \ \& \ [z]_{n^0} = t\} \leftrightarrow t = m^0]$$

are deducible in A.

Theorem 33ª. If $n! \neq m$, then the formulas mentioned in Theorem 32ª are refutable in A.

Theorem 34ª. The formulas $Form(g^0)$, $Ths(g^0)$, and $Logid(g^0)$ are deducible or refutable in A according as they are true or false.

The proofs of Theorems 28ª–34ª are left to the reader. In several cases it will be convenient to use the proof of Theorem 22ª as a paradigm.
We shall now establish a few facts which will prove helpful when we turn to the problem of proving Theorem 34.

Theorem 35ª. If from a set K of premisses a certain conclusion Z is *not* deducible, then the set K is consistent.

Proof. Suppose K permits the deduction of two conclusions U and $\bar{U}$, and let Z be any formula. Since the formula $U \to (\bar{U} \to Z)$ is a thesis, K permits the following deduction of Z:

$$K$$
$$\vdots$$
$$U$$
$$\vdots$$
$$\bar{U}$$
$$U \to (\bar{U} \to Z)$$
$$\bar{U} \to Z$$
$$Z$$

Conversely, if K does not permit the deduction of Z it follows that the set K must be consistent.

Theorem 36[a]. The formula $S0 = 0$ is not deducible from the axioms (A1–8).

Proof. Let us construct the semantic tableau for the sequent:

$$(XVII)–(XX), (A1–8)/S0 = 0$$

in accordance with the rules for elementary logic with equality and terms as set forth in Section 37, *sub* (5).

We observe that none of the formulas involved in the construction demands an application of reduction schemata (vi[b]) or (vij[a]); therefore, only numerical terms are used in applications of reduction schema (vi[a]).

Furthermore, the valuation w introduced in Section 17, *sub* (5) can be extended in a straightforward manner to those quantifier-free formulas which arise. Under the valuation w which results, none of these formulas is wrongly placed.

Hence, it follows from the properties of the semantic tableaux for sentential logic that the semantic tableau cannot be closed. It follows that in the framework of elementary logic with equality and terms, the formula $S0 = 0$ is not deducible from the axioms (A1–8).

Therefore, the deductive theory developed by means of elementary logic with equality and terms on the basis of the axioms (A1–8) is consistent.

Theorem 37[a]. The formula $S0 = 0$ is not deducible from the axioms (A1–9).

Proof. We now construct the semantic tableau for the sequent:

$$(XVII)–(XX), (A1–9)/S0 = 0 .$$

As compared to Theorem 36[a] a complication arises from the fact that now the 'treatment' of axiom (A9), or $(x)[x = 0 \vee (Ey)\{x = Sy\}]$, introduces the formulas $t = 0$ and $(Ey)\{t = Sy\}$, the latter of which demands the introduction of a 'fresh' parameter p; this parameter will appear in terms t' involved in later applications of rule (vi[a]).

This complication is overcome by extending the valuation w, first to all parameters which appear in the tableau, then to all terms, and finally to all formulas in the tableau. This is accomplished as follows.

Let $p_1, p_2, \ldots, p_j, \ldots$ be the parameters in the order of their introduction and suppose the numerical values $w(p_1), w(p_2), \ldots, w(p_{j-1})$ have been suitably determined. The parameter p_j will be introduced through the 'treatment' of a formula $(Ey)\{t_j = y\}$, where t_j contains no parameters except $p_1, p_2, \ldots, p_{j-1}$. It follows that $w(t_j)$ can be computed by virtue of stipulations (i)–(iv) in Section 17, *sub* (5).

Now if (a) $w(t_j) = 0$, we take $w(p_j) = 0$, and if (b) $w(t_j) = k \neq 0$, we take $w(p_j) = k - 1$. In case (a), we have $w(t_j = 0) = 2$ and in case (b), $w(t_j = Sp_j) = 2$. It follows that at any rate:

$$w[t_j = 0 \vee (Ey)\{t_j = Sy\}] = 2.$$

It is easy to see that all axioms (A1–9) are true under the valuation w thus extended. Therefore, we may again conclude that none of the initial formulas in the tableau are wrongly placed. So the tableau will never be closed, and hence the formula $S0 = 0$ cannot be deduced from axioms (A1–9) by means of elementary logic with equality and terms. This completes our proof.

Using Theorems 35^a and 37^a as lemmas, we easily prove Theorem 34 in Section 17.

Remark. According to Theorem 37 in Section 18, neither the above argument nor any other proof of the consistency of the deductive system A can be stated within the system A itself. As far as the above argument is concerned, it is not difficult to see why it would not fit into the system A: it involves a certain recursion for which the axioms (A1–9) clearly make no allowance.

42. THE INTERPOLATION THEOREM OF CRAIG-LYNDON

Suppose that a certain formula:

$$A \to B$$

is a thesis and that A is built from atoms $A'(\ldots), A''(\ldots), \ldots, C'(\ldots),$ $C''(\ldots)$, whereas B is built from atoms $B'(\ldots), B''(\ldots), \ldots, C'(\ldots),$ $C''(\ldots), \ldots$. In other words, the parameters $A', A'', \ldots$ appear in A but not in B, the parameters B', B'', ... appear in B but not in A, and the parameters C', C'', ... appear both in A and in B.

(1) Since $A \rightarrow B$ is a thesis and hence a tautology by Theorem 21, the semantic tableau for $\emptyset/A \rightarrow B$ is closed, and so is also the semantic tableau for A/B. The closure of a semantic tableau results from that of all its final subtableaux. The closure of a final subtableau results from the appearance of *equiform* formulas (formulas typographically alike), say X and Y, in its left and right columns. Four cases may be distinguished:
  (i) X originates from A, Y originates from B;
 (ij) Y originates from A, X originates from B;
(iij) both X and Y originate from A;
(iv) both X and Y originate from B.

(2) We now construct for each subtableau a certain formula which represents the *sentential power* of A in that subtableau. If the subtableau is final, we shall have in the above four cases, respectively: (i) X, (ij) $\bar{Y}$, (iij) Q [contradiction], and (iv) R [tautology].

(3) If a subtableau is not final and splits into subtableaux in which the sentential power of A is respectively P_1 and P_2, then the power of A in the original subtableau is (a) if the splitting is due to A or to another formula originating from it, $P_1 \vee P_2$ (b) if the splitting is due to B or to another formula originating from it, $P_1 \& P_2$.
In applying this rule, we replace:

$$P \vee Q \text{ or } Q \vee P \text{ by } P,$$
$$P \& Q \text{ or } Q \& P \text{ by } Q,$$
$$P \vee R \text{ or } R \vee P \text{ by } R,$$
$$P \& R \text{ or } R \& P \text{ by } P.$$

(4) It is easy to see that if the power of A in the given tableau is Q, then $\bar{A}$ is a thesis; and if the power of A in the given tableau is R, then B is a thesis. We suppose that neither $\bar{A}$ nor B is a thesis; so the power of A in the given tableau can be neither Q nor R.

(5) Starting from the formula P which represents the sentential power

of A in the tableau, we now construct a formula P^0 which represents the *quantificational power* of the formula A in the tableau as follows. Let $p_1, p_2, p_3, \ldots, p_k, \ldots$ be those parameters which appear in P in the order in which they have been introduced. Then P^0 will be obtained from P by first replacing these parameters by variables $v_1, v_2, v_3, \ldots, v_k$, and then placing quantifiers $(Qv_1)(Qv_2)(Qv_3) \ldots (Qv_k) \ldots$ in front of the expression which results. If p_k was introduced on account of the 'treatment' of the formula A or of a formula originating from it, then (Qv_k) is (Ev_k), otherwise (Qv_k) is (v_k).

(6) It is easy to see that P^0 represents the quantificational power of A in the given tableau in the following precise sense: the semantic tableau for the sequent P^0/B is closed.

(7) Furthermore, we may ask for a formula Q^0 which, similarly, represents the quantificational power of B in the given tableau. Now if we try to adapt the idea which guided us in constructing P^0, then we observe that the very same formula P^0, if placed in the right column, will represent the quantificational power of B as well. In other words, the semantic tableau for the sequent A/P^0 is also closed.

(8) By its construction, the formula P^0 contains only parameters $C', C'', \ldots$ which appear both in A and in B. Moreover, P^0 contains a positive (a negative) occurrence of an atom $C'(\ldots), C''(\ldots), \ldots$ only if both A and B contain positive (negative) occurrences of that atom. An occurrence of $C'(\ldots), C''(\ldots), \ldots$ in P^0, A, or B is said to be *positive* if the construction of a semantic tableau leads to the appearance of that atom in the same column in which P^0, A, or B appears; if the atom appears in the conjugate column, then its occurrence in P^0, A, or B is said to be *negative*. So we have:

Theorem 38ª (W. Craig, 1953; R. C. Lyndon, 1957). If a formula:

$$A \to B$$

is a thesis, whereas neither $\bar{A}$ nor B are theses, then we can find a formula P^0 containing positive (negative) occurrences only of those atoms of which both A and B contain positive (negative) occurrences, and such that both:

$$A \to P^0 \quad \text{and} \quad P^0 \to B$$

are theses.

(9) Let us now return to the discussion in Section 23, *sub* (4). Let G be the conjunction of all formulas in K', and H the conjunction of all formulas in K''. If $(K', K'', \bar{Z})$ is inconsistent, then the semantic tableau for the sequent:

$$(G, H)/F'(p_1, p_2, \ldots, p_k) \to F''(p_1, p_2, \ldots, p_k)$$

is closed and hence the formula:

$$[G \,\&\, F'(p_1, p_2, \ldots, p_k)] \to \{H \to F''(p_1, p_2, \ldots, p_k)\}$$

is a thesis. Let P^0 be the corresponding formula as described in Theorem 38[a]. Then the formulas:

$$[G \,\&\, F'(p_1, p_2, \ldots, p_k)] \to P^0, \quad P^0 \to \{H \to F''(p_1, p_2, \ldots, p_k)\}$$

and hence (since in the second formula we may replace F'' throughout by F') also the formula:

$$P^0 \to \{G \to F'(p_1, p_2, \ldots, p_k)\}$$

must be theses. It follows that:

$$G \to \{P^0 \leftrightarrow F'(p_1, p_2, \ldots, p_k)\}$$

is a thesis.

(10) So clearly the parameter F' is provably definable and the formula P^0 provides a suitable definiëns. Therefore we have:

Theorem 39[a] (E. W. Beth, 1953). If a primitive notion F is independent with respect to the other primitive notions A, B, ... of a deductive discipline T, then there are two models $\mathbf{M}'$ and $\mathbf{M}''$ of T by which this fact can be demonstrated in accordance with Padoa's method.

LIST OF SCHEMATA AND AXIOMS

BIBLIOGRAPHY

For obvious reasons, the following bibliography has been split into several parts. The items under (A) are nearly all considerably more advanced than those under (B); for the greater part, they can be successfully studied only by professional logicians.

(A) SOURCES

BETH, E. W. *The Foundations of Mathematics* (Studies in Logic), Amsterdam 1959.
BOUVÈRE, K. L. DE, *A Method in Proofs of Undefinability*, Amsterdam 1959.
CARNAP, R. *Studies in Semantics*, I-II, Cambridge, Mass., 1942, 1943.
GENTZEN, G. Untersuchungen über das logische Schliessen, *Mathematische Zeitschrift 39* (1934).
—, *Recherches sur la déduction logique*, trad. et comm. par R. FEYS et J. LADRIÈRE, Paris 1955.
GUILLAUME, M. Rapports entre calculs propositionnels modaux et topologie impliqués par certaines extensions de la méthode des tableaux sémantiques, *C. R. Acad. des Sciences* (Paris) *246* (1958).
HENKIN, L. Fragments of propositional calculus, *Journal of Symbolic Logic 14* (1949).
HERBRAND, J. *Recherches sur la théorie de la démonstration* (Thèse), Paris 1930.
HILBERT, D. & P. BERNAYS, *Grundlagen der Mathematik*, I-II, Berlin 1934, 1938.
HINTIKKA, K. J. J. *Two Papers on Symbolic Logic*, Helsinki 1955.
JASKOWSKI, S. *On the Rules of Suppositions in Formal Logic* (Studia Logica), Warsaw 1934.
KALMAR, L. Über die Axiomatisierbarkeit des Aussagenkalküls, *Acta scient. math. 7* (1934).
KANGER, *Probability in Logic* (Stockholm Studies in Philosophy), Stockholm 1957.
KLEENE, S. C. *Introduction to Metamathematics*, Amsterdam-Groningen 1952.
KRIPKE, S. A completeness theorem in modal logic, *Journal of Symbolic Logic 24* (1959).
LIS, Z. Wynikanie semantyczne a wynikanie formalne, *Studia Logica 10* (1960).
LORENZEN, P. Ein dialogisches Konstruktivitätskriterium, in: *Infinitistic Methods,* Proceedings of the Symposium on Foundations of Mathematics (Warsaw, 2–9 September 1959), Oxford-Warszawa 1961.
ROSENBLOOM, P. C. *The Elements of Mathematical Logic*, New York 1950.
SCHMIDT, H. A. *Mathematische Gesetze der Logik*, I: Vorlesungen über Aussagenlogik, Berlin-Göttingen-Heidelberg 1960.
SCHRÖTER, K. Die Vollständigkeit der die Implikation enthaltenden zweiwertigen Aussagenkalküle und Prädikatenkalküle der ersten Stufe, *Zeitschr. f. math. Logik und Grundlagen d. Math. 3* (1957).

164

BIBLIOGRAPHY

SCHÜTTE, K. Ein System des verknüpfenden Schliessens, *Archiv f. Math. Logik und Grundlagenforschung 2* (1956).

TARSKI, A. *Logic, Semantics, Metamathematics* – Papers from 1923 to 1938, Oxford 1956, in particular: IV. Investigations into the sentential calculus (by J. ŁUKASIEWICZ and A. TARSKI), and: X. Some methodological investigations on the definability of concepts.

WAJSBERG, M. Beiträge zum Metaaussagenkalkül I, *Monatsh. f. Math. und Physik 42* (1935).

Concerning the Construction of a '*Logic Theory Machine*':

BETH, E. W. On Machines Which Prove Theorems, *Simon Stevin 32* (1958).

DUNHAM, B., R. FRIDSHAL, & G. L. SWARD, A nonheuristic program for proving elementary logical theorems, *Proceed. of the First Int. Conference on Information Processing*, Paris 1959.

GELERNTER, H. Theorem Proving by Machine, in: *Summaries of talks presented at the Summer Institute of Symbolic Logic in 1957 at Cornell University* (mimeographed).

—, Realization of a Geometry Theorem Proving Machine (mimeographed preprint for limited circulation).

GELERNTER, H. L. & N. ROCHESTER, Intelligent Behavior in Problem-Solving Machines, *IBM Journal of Research and Development 2* (1958).

GILMORE, P. C. A program for the production of proofs of theorems derivable within the first order predicate calculus from axioms, *Proceed. of the First Int. Conference.*

—, A proof method for quantification theory: Its justification and realization, *IBM Journal 4* (1960).

MCCULLOCH, W. C. & W. PITTS, A Logical Calculus of the Ideas Immanent in Nervous Activity, *Bull. of Math. Biophysics 5* (1943).

MINSKY, M. L. Heuristic Aspects of the Artificial Intelligence Problem, *Lincoln Laboratory Report 34–55* (1956).

MORE, JR., Trenchard, *Deductive Logic for Automata* (Thesis for M. Sc., M.I.T., 1957, not published).

NEWELL, A. & H. A. SIMON, The Logic Theory Machine, *IRE Transactions on Information Theory, IT–2* (1956).

NEWELL, A., J. C. SHAW, & H. A. SIMON, Empirical Explorations of the Logic Theory Machine, *Proceed. of the Western Joint Computer Conf.* (1957).

POLYA, G. *Mathematics and Plausible Inference*, I–II, Princeton, N. J., 1954.

PRAWITZ, D., H. PRAWITZ, & N. VOGHERA, A Mechanical Proof Procedure and its Realization in an Electronic Computer, *Journal of the Ass. for Computing Machinery 7* (1960).

PRAWITZ, D. An Improved Proof Procedure, *Theoria 26* (1960).

ROBINSON, A. Proving a Theorem (as done by Man, Logician, or Machine), in: *Summaries of talks.*

WANG, HAO, Towards Mechanical Mathematics, *IBM Journal 4* (1960).

Concerning the Problem of '*Circuit Synthesis*':

BURKS, A. W. & J. B. WRIGHT, Theory of Logical Nets, *Proceedings of the IRE 41* (1953).

FORMAL METHODS

CHURCH, A. Applications of Recursive Arithmetic to the Problem of Circuit Synthesis, in: *Summaries of talks.*
FITCH, F. B. Representation of Sequential Circuits in Combinatory Logic, *Philosophy of Science 25* (1958).
FRIEDMANN, Joyce, Some Results in Church's Restricted Recursive Arithmetic, *Journal of Symbolic Logic 22* (1958).
GOTÔ, Motinori, Application of Logical Mathematics to the Theory of Relay Networks, *The Japan Science Review 1* (1950).
HARTREE, D. R. *Calculating Instruments and Machines,* Urbana, Ill., 1949.
KLEENE, S. C. Representation of Events in Nerve Nets and Finite Automata, in: *Automata Studies,* Princeton 1956.
MCCULLOCH, W. S. & W. PITTS, A Logical Calculus of the Ideas Immanent in Nervous Activity, *Bull. of Math. Biophysics 5* (1943).
REED, I. S. Symbolic Synthesis of Digital Computers, *Proceed. of the Ass. for Computing Machinery* (1952).

(B) RECOMMENDED READING

BASSON, A. H. & D. J. O'CONNOR, *Introduction to Symbolic Logic,* 2nd ed., London 1957.
BOCHENSKI, J. M. *A Precis of Mathematical Logic* (Synthese Library), Dordrecht 1959. – A valuable survey of the various more important domains of modern logic.
CHURCH, A. *Introduction to Mathematical Logic,* I. Princeton, N. J., 1956. – Detailed and painstaking treatment of the fundamental parts of logic, in particular of sentential logic; actually this book has been one of our main sources.
CURRY, H. B. The Interpretation of Formalized Implication, *Theoria 25* (1959). – To be compared with the discussion in Section 2, *sub* (1)–(3).
FEIGL, H. & W. SELLARS, *Readings in Philosophical Analysis,* New York 1949. – Collection of papers showing the importance of modern logic for contemporary philosophy.
HERMES, H. *Aufzählbarkeit, Entscheidbarkeit, Berechenbarkeit,* Berlin-Göttingen-Heidelberg 1961.
KANGER, S. *Handbok i Logik,* del I: Logisk konsekvens, Stockholm 1957.
LEBLANC, H. *An Introduction to Deductive Logic,* New York-London 1955. – A thorough elementary treatment of sentential logic and of the theory of quantification.
LINSKY, L. *Semantics and the Philosophy of Language,* Urbana, Ill., 1952. – Collection of papers on the philosophy of language from the viewpoint of modern logic.
PRIOR, A. N. *Formal Logic,* Oxford 1955. – Gives a detailed exposition of the completeness proofs for sentential logic by Quine and by Wajsberg.
QUINE, W. V. *Methods of Logic,* revised edition, New York 1959. – Elegant treatment of sentential logic and of the theory of quantification with fascinating 'glimpses beyond'.
REICHENBACH, H. *The Rise of Scientific Philosophy,* Berkeley, Calif., 1951. – Survey of the domain of the philosophy of science.
RUSSELL, B. *Introduction to Mathematical Philosophy,* London 1919. – Exposition of Russell's ideas on this subject, which have strongly influenced the development of our domain.

166

STEGMÜLLER, W. *Das Wahrheitsproblem und die Idee der Semantik*, Wien 1957. – Detailed account of the contributions by Tarski and by Carnap, with a summary exposition of the discussions which they elicited.

—, *Unvollständigkeit und Unentscheidbarkeit*, Wien 1959. – Detailed exposition of the ideas and results of Gödel, Church, Kleene, Rosser, with a view to their philosophical significance; mainly based upon Kleene's *Introduction*.

TARSKI, A. *Introduction to Logic*, 2nd ed., New York 1946. – Highly successful elementary text by one of the outstanding authorities; deals in particular with the construction of deductive theories; also available in Dutch, French, German, Hebrew, Polish, Russian, and Spanish.

WEYL, H. *Philosophy of Mathematics and Natural Science*, 2nd ed., Princeton 1949. – Interesting discussion on a rather advanced level.

(C) PERIODICALS

Archiv für Mathematische Logik und Grundlagenforschung (Stuttgart, *4*–1959).

British Journal for the Philosophy of Science (Edinburgh, *12*–1961).

Journal of Symbolic Logic (published for the Association for Symbolic Logic by N.V. Erven P. Noordhoff, Groningen, *25*–1960). – Of special importance on account of the review section which provides a current bibliography of the whole domain.

Logique et Analyse (Publication trimestrielle du Centre National Belge de recherches de Logique, Nauwelaerts, Louvain-Paris, nouvelle série, *4*–1961).

Studia Logica (Polska Akademia Nauk, Komitet Filozoficzny, *10*–1960).

Synthese (Dordrecht-Holland, *13*–1961).

Zeitschrift für mathematische Logik und Grundlagen der Mathematik (Berlin-D.D.R., *6*–1961).

INDEX OF AUTHORS AND SUBJECTS